D0178587

or before

The Euthanasia Issue

ISSUES
(formerly Issues for the Nineties)

Volume 4

Editor

Craig Donnellan

Independence

Educational Publishers
Cambridge

First published by Independence
PO Box 295
Cambridge CB1 3XP
England

British Library Cataloguing in Publication Data
The Euthanasia Issue – (Issues Series)
I. Donnellan, Craig II. Series
179.7

ISBN 1 86168 176 3

Printed in Great Britain
The Burlington Press
Cambridge

Typeset by
Claire Boyd

Cover
The illustration on the front cover is by
Pumpkin House.

CONTENTS

Introduction

The Euthanasia Issue is the fourth volume in the **Issues** series. The aim of this series is to offer up-to-date information about important issues in our world.

The Euthanasia Issue examines the moral and medical views of euthanasia and also looks at the issue of living wills.

The information comes from a wide variety of sources and includes:
Government reports and statistics
Newspaper reports and features
Magazine articles and surveys
Literature from lobby groups
and charitable organisations.

It is hoped that, as you read about the many aspects of the issues explored in this book, you will critically evaluate the information presented. It is important that you decide whether you are being presented with facts or opinions. Does the writer give a biased or an unbiased report? If an opinion is being expressed, do you agree with the writer?

The Euthanasia Issue offers a useful starting-point for those who need convenient access to information about the many issues involved. However, it is only a starting-point. At the back of the book is a list of organisations which you may want to contact for further information.

*****

creasingly questioned. Tube-feeding is not usually unduly burdensome, and only becomes futile if it no longer enables a patient to receive nourishment. Even if the provision of food and water requires medical assistance, they are not intended to cure illness but are the basic means of sustaining life, which it is unjust to deny anyone on grounds of their disability.

* The persistent vegetative state is increasingly referred to simply as the *vegetative state*. The use of *vegetative* in these expressions is gravely misleading since it suggests that a person in such a condition has somehow ceased to be human.

Advance directives

Advance directives are statements by a patient which typically contain instructions that, in the event of certain conditions arising (such as paralysis, incontinence, inability to communicate, the need for artificial life support), treatment should not be given. An advance directive is not necessarily a request for euthanasia, but such statements can be used to demand that doctors bring about the patient's death by, for example, specifying that tube-feeding should be withheld. For this reason, advance directives, which, in this context, are often referred to as living wills, have become an important part of the campaign of the pro-euthanasia lobby. Legislation for living wills would facilitate the introduction of euthanasia, and this is the principal reason why SPUC opposes moves in Parliament to make advance directives legally binding.

Doctors might act on an advance directive in circumstances which the patient did not foresee, or misinterpret the patient's wishes. While advance directives may be helpful to doctors in forming an impression of the patient's preferences, if they are binding, they are liable to tie the hands of doctors, preventing them from acting in the patient's best interests. A patient may not realise that withholding treatment will not necessarily lead to an earlier death with less suffering. It may, in fact, lead to a bed-bound state with greater impairment of health.

Ascertaining when life ends

The criterion of brain stem death has been used to determine that death was imminent and inevitable, so that treatment could be discontinued. However, there has been a widespread tendency to regard brain stem death as signifying death itself. Some go further and suggest that patients with certain forms of brain damage, such as persistent vegetative state, should be regarded as dead.

There is increasing concern among pro-life doctors and ethicists that a patient should not be regarded as dead until there is evidence of both brain stem death and the end of other vital functions. This would safeguard against ending the lives of patients who had volunteered for organ donation before natural death had occurred.

• The above information is an extract from SPUC's web site which can be found at www.spuc.org.uk

Brief answers to five objections

Information from the South Australian Voluntary Euthanasia Society

Objection 1 – We cannot always be sure that the patient wants to die.
Answer: There are no absolute certainties in medical practice but this does not eliminate the need, at times, for doctors to make life and death decisions. Faced with a request for euthanasia, the doctor would follow prescribed guidelines which would include being satisfied that the strength and persistence of the request left no reasonable doubt as to the patient's firm and rational intention.

Objection 2 – We cannot always be sure that there is no possibility of cure or return to an acceptable quality of life.
Answer: Cures take years to discover, test and become generally available. The doctor would discuss the prognosis so that the patient could make an informed decision as to whether a cure or remission was worth waiting for.

Objection 3 – Palliative care is now so effective that no one need ever ask for euthanasia.
Answer: There are acknowledged limits to palliative care. There are still cases in which pain cannot be satisfactorily controlled, but of greater concern is the loss of faculties and descent into total dependence on others over a lengthy period as a miserable prelude to death.

Objection 4 – Efforts to find cures and to improve palliative care will be discouraged.
Answer: The will to live is so strong that no one wishes to die while their life can still have reasonable quality. There will always be pressure to find cures and improve treatment. Euthanasia would only be an option for those whom current medical skills could not help. The incentive to perfect those skills would remain.

Objection 5 – It is always wrong to shorten life deliberately.
Answer: Those who have this conviction would be free to abstain, either as doctor or patient, but should not deny the option to those who do not share their belief. Most people hold that life should not be taken unlawfully: they accept that there are circumstances in which the taking of life may be justified and that the law should provide for these.

• Further information on this and related issues is available from: Hon Secretary, SAVES, PO Box 2151, Kent Town, SA 5071, Australia

Physician-assisted suicide

Information from the Christian Medical Fellowship. By Kathryn Myers

Every time that UK politicians have considered euthanasia, they have concluded that it is wrong and that it would be unhelpful to make it legal within our society. Some people are now suggesting that we consider physician-assisted suicide (PAS). However, although some doctors say that it 'feels' different, in reality PAS is simply euthanasia, one step removed.

Being in pain that is so severe that it occupies your life and being incapable of relieving it, is many people's worst nightmare. Similarly some worry that they will reach the point in life where they would like to die in relative peace, only to find that they are forced to receive massive and intrusive medical intervention that desperately attempts to prolong their life. Others panic about lying in a bed for months or years, while incapable of making any responses to family, friends or hospital staff.

These sorts of fears are leading people to ask whether there is a place for physician-assisted suicide (PAS). At first sight this call appears to be driven by compassion for the individual and to be a way of respecting their rights. However, making facilities available to help someone kill themselves may be more likely to reduce the respect that we have for human life in general and is not the most appropriate way of helping that person.

Christians believe that men and women are made 'in the image of God' and one of the results of this is that their lives are highly valuable. A consequence is that God prohibits anyone from deliberately taking the life of another human being. Opinions vary, but some Christians say that there are exceptional circumstances where it is morally allowable to take life – the exceptions being extreme judicial situations, and in a 'just war'. The Jewish and Islamic faiths have similar prohibitions.

The definitions of euthanasia and PAS [see box] emphasise the moral, ethical and legal concept of 'intention'. There is a world of difference between a medical act designed to end life, such as a lethal injection, and withdrawing a treatment which is ineffective or inappropriate. One is killing. The other is good practice. The medical and legal professions have always recognised the difference.

A call for compassion

Compassion, the feeling of distress and pity for the suffering or misfortune of another person, is a major argument for PAS.

However, the compassion argument is misplaced, because the best way to show compassion for a person is to care for them. A combination of the hospice movement and advanced medical technology now allows pain and distressing symptoms of disease to be adequately alleviated in all but the most extreme cases. Experience shows that once people are comfortable they often change their minds about wanting to end their lives.

Two definitions

The CMF defines euthanasia as the intentional killing, by act or omission, of a person whose life is felt not to be worth living.

The word comes from the Greek *eu-thanatos*, which literally means 'well-death' or easy-death. It is sometimes referred to as 'mercy killing.' In the medical environment it is normally used when a doctor prescribes and gives a lethal dose of medication.

Physician-assisted suicide is where the doctor prescribes a lethal medication, but the person administers the dose himself or herself.

The best way of giving a person true dignity, and respecting their value, is to care for them and make their life as comfortable and fulfilling as possible. This is a much stronger action than simply giving up on them and promoting their death.

In many respects, when death comes, the more natural it is the more dignity it affords.

Asking to be autonomous

Some people have demanded the right to PAS (and euthanasia) because they claim to put strong emphasis on the rights to autonomy (self-determination). However, having the right of autonomy is not easy to define.

In recent years, there has been a healthy move away from medical paternalism, with its restrictive idea that the doctor knows best. But as John Donne said, 'No man is an island, entire of itself; everyone is a continent, a part of the main.'[1] The actions of a person who takes his or her own life have profound effects on those who live through the tragedy. That person exerting their right to autonomy has removed the same right from the survivors.

In addition, the free exercise of autonomy with respect to PAS could decrease our notion of the value or worth of vulnerable people.

Autonomy is fine so far as it reflects the unique individuality of each human being, created 'in the image of God', and ultimately accountable to him. But to use our autonomy responsibly, we need to balance our rights (the things we may do), responsibilities (the things we must do) and restrictions (the things we must not do). Autonomy is not therefore the same as saying that people have the right to do whatever they like.

Furthermore, depression, confusion, unrelieved physical symptoms, a sense of 'being a burden', conscious and unconscious pressures from family, friends, carers or society could all remove the person's true autonomy. It seems highly likely that one or more of these factors would be operating in the vast majority of requests for PAS. The problem is that when a patient who is in pain or suffering asks to die there is good reason to think that the request is compelled by the pain, and not in fact freely chosen.[2,3]

Finally, unlike suicide, PAS is not a private act. By definition, PAS requires a doctor to be involved, and so the patient's decision impinges on the doctor's autonomy.

Don't want to be a burden –
There is a real danger of people asking to end their lives because they don't want to be a burden to families or friends. The burden could be expressed in terms of time, money or even the emotional cost of caring for someone who is in need.

In asking for PAS people may be hoping to relieve the stress placed on their families. They may also feel that the amount of time and money that the health service is devoting to them would be better spent on others. If PAS was allowed there would be a real danger of people being persuaded to ask for it. This could be by overt cajoling, or through deliberate neglect of the family [see 'Experience overseas' below].

Healthcare professionals may also add to the pressure by their attitudes towards the resources being used to look after the person. In reality, it is very difficult for family members or even involved health-care professionals to make appropriate judgements about the value of another person's life.

However, the hallmark of a healthy society is how well it looks after its weakest and most vulnerable members. Rather than looking to provide a 'way out' for these people, we should be looking for more effective ways of caring for them.

Trust and service
Doctors have a privileged relation-ship with their patients. It is one that is fundamentally built on trust – trust that the doctor will always act in a way that seeks to do them no harm. This relationship has been recognised and fostered in a series of

ancient and modern oaths and codes of practice.

Legalisation of PAS would give the doctors enormous new powers over life and death. This has the real possibility of removing the patient's innate trust in their doctor.

Policing any law allowing PAS would be extremely difficult, particularly because the key witness in any inquiry would be dead.

At the same time, society would start to lose the idea of the benefits that can come from learning to serve and care for people in need. What could start off as an idea to modernise the way we look at care, could all too easily mean that we lose medical or nursing facilities and our abilities to care for those who are in need but do not want to cut their lives short.

More than that, PAS could start to alter the way that society views both death and disability and, as a consequence, society could become less caring all round. People who are difficult or costly to care for may be seen as second-rate citizens. We could also become detached from reality, believing that there are quick-fix solutions to all difficult problems.

The law and suicide
There is a popular misconception that the 1961 Suicide Act gave someone the right to take their own life. In fact the Act decriminalised the act of suicide, but every effort is made to prevent a person from committing it.

The general principle is that people who want to kill themselves

---

Oaths and declarations
For more than 2,000 years medical practitioners have used oaths and declarations as a way of committing themselves to particular ethical principles. Studying them shows a central respect for the value of human life.

Hippocratic Oath (ca. 400 BC)
'I will give no deadly medicine to anyone if asked, nor suggest such counsel.'

Declaration of Geneva (1948)
'I will maintain the utmost respect for human life from the time of conception; even under threat I will not use my medical knowledge contrary to the laws of humanity.'

International Code of Medical Ethics (1949)
'A doctor must always bear in mind the importance of preserving human life from the time of conception until death.'

Declaration of Oslo (1970)
This declaration reaffirmed the 'utmost respect for human life from the time of conception'.

Statement of Marbella (1992)
'Physician-assisted suicide, like euthanasia, is unethical and must be condemned by the medical profession.'

are considered to be ill and in need of treatment and care.

This is recognised in the UK government's White Paper on health entitled *Saving Lives: Our Healthier Nation*[4], in which one of the key goals is to reduce the rate of suicide by 'at least a fifth' by the year 2010. Introducing PAS would be an obstacle to achieving this goal.

Experience overseas

Few countries allow any form of PAS or euthanasia. The principal exception is The Netherlands, where although it is not allowed by statute, the law accepts a standard defence from doctors who have adhered to official guidelines. These require that the patient's request was voluntary and that their distress was un-relievable. It is not a condition that the patient is terminally ill or that the suffering is physical.

When a committee from the House of Lords visited The Nether-lands to see how well their system was working they were not im-pressed.[5] Official Dutch statistics show that of the 3,000 people who died by euthanasia, there was no evidence of any voluntary request having been made by the person in over 1,000 cases.[6]

This shows that PAS can be the start of a slippery slope that leads to unrequested euthanasia.

In the USA all of the States with the exception of Oregon forbid any form of mercy killing. On October 27, 1997, Oregon legalised PAS in the face of opposition from the American Medical Association as well as church leaders. The Death and Dignity Act allows for patients who have a significantly and irreversibly diminished quality of life to obtain drugs from their doctor that can help them commit suicide.

Official figures suggest that fifteen people died by lethal overdose in 1998 in Oregon.[7] But the report points to flaws in the legislation that could lead to under-reporting. For example physicians have the option of not reporting a case if it involved the violation of a guideline.

Debate in the USA was re-kindled when in April 1999, a court in Michigan sentenced Dr Jack Kevorkian to a minimum of 10 years in gaol for the second degree murder of 52-year-old Thomas Youk, a man who had amyotrophic lateral sclerosis. Kevorkian, who has campaigned for the legalisation of both euthanasia and PAS, claims to have assisted in 130 suicides.

Positive provision

There is a genuine contradiction between good medicine and killing people. The provision of hospices and palliative care have clearly shown that there is a positive alternative to PAS which involves killing pain rather than killing patients. However, that provision comes at a cost. The House of Lords Ethics Committee concluded that: 'Rejection of euthanasia as an option for the individual entails a compelling social responsibility to care adequately for those who are elderly, dying or disabled.'

Of course everybody wants to have a good death for themselves, their loved ones and their patients, but a good death is not the same as simply having a convenient one.

References
1   John Donne (1623) *Devotions*, 17
2   Jochemsen H & Keown J (1999) *J Med Ethics*; 25: 16-21
3   Campbell N (1999) *J Med Ethics*; 25: 242-4
4   *Saving Lives: Our Healthier Nation* (1999) CM4386
5   *Report of the Select Committee on Medical Ethics* – Session 1993-94. HL Paper 21-1
6   van der Maas et al (1991) *Lancet*; 338: 669-674
7   Chin et al (1999) *New England Journal of Medicine*; 340: 577-83

A case history

Once depression and other symptoms have been treated, patients may change their minds:

Sixty-five year old John was found to have lung cancer following a chest X-ray carried out to investigate a bad cough. The cancer was advanced and could not be cured.

Over the next few weeks, John became breathless when he walked and developed pain in his chest. He also became withdrawn and depressed and worried more and more about the stress his illness was causing his wife.

For several weeks he repeatedly asked his GP to help him to die because he could see no point in carrying on with more suffering. The GP prescribed stronger painkillers, antidepressant tablets, and referred John to a specialist hospice nurse. She visited him and his wife regularly at home and listened to their anxieties and fears. She helped to adjust his medication until the pain was controlled most of the time and his spirits had lifted. She arranged for John to visit the hospice day centre one day a week so that his wife could have a rest.

John talked with other patients there and took up an interest in painting. He stopped asking to die, even though his condition was gradually deteriorating.

He died at home three months later, having told the staff how glad he was not to have died when he had wanted to, but to have been given a chance 'to live', even though he was dying.

Further reading

Euthanasia – An edited collection of articles from the Journal of the Christian Medical Fellowship.

Euthanasia and Physician-assisted Suicide – for and against (1998) Dworkin, Frey & Bok. CUP – New York.

Previous CMF Files include:
No. 1 *Introduction to ethics*
No. 2 *Animal experimentation*
No. 3 *Christian views on ethics*
No. 4 *Adolescent sexuality*
No. 5 *The ethics of caring*
No. 6 *Artificial reproduction*
No. 7 *When to withdraw or withhold treatment*
No. 8 *Dependence and addiction*

These can be found at: www.cmf.org.uk/ethics/brief/ brief.htm or ordered free from CMF.

• Dr Kathryn Myders is a locum Consultant in Palliative Medicine at the Mildmay Hospital, London. The above information is by the Christian Medical Fellowship. See page 41 for their address details.

Dutch pass euthanasia bill

Senators end nearly 30 years of debate despite protests by Christian groups

The Netherlands became the first country to legalise euthanasia last night in a move expected to encourage several other European countries to follow suit.

As protesters gathered outside the wood-panelled chamber of the Dutch upper house of parliament, the country's 75 senators approved the bill to allow doctors to end the lives of terminally ill patients in certain highly prescribed circumstances. With one senator absent, the upper house voted by 46 to 28 to introduce the law, a result that both opponents and supporters of mercy killing had agreed was a foregone conclusion.

Parties in favour of euthanasia control 46 of the senate's 75 seats, over 90% of the Dutch population supports the bill, and the practice has been taking place informally for decades anyway.

But that did not stop opponents of the new legislation protesting against the move yesterday in a vain attempt to persuade the senators to cause an upset by blocking the bill. Christian activists sang hymns in the senate courtyard while at least 5,000 people, many of them schoolchildren, staged a silent march from the railway station to the town's picturesque Plein Square.

They listened with rapt attention as religious leaders and Calvinist politicians condemned euthanasia in Old Testament terms.

Two protesters in black Balaclavas and white laboratory coats clutched oversized syringes supporting a banner proclaiming that 'euthanasia will always be murder'.

One of the men, Oskar, said he was a Catholic historian and argued that the Dutch government had used a barrage of propaganda to 'brainwash' the population into supporting euthanasia.

He told the *Guardian*: 'It was a propaganda war and they won. It was like Goebbels and the Nazis and that's how they brainwashed the population.

*By Andrew Osborn
and Sarah Boseley*

'Thou shalt not kill is an essential commandment for every society. There are so many old people in this country and they want to get rid of them. I worry about it a lot.'

> *The decision to decriminalise the practice in the Netherlands could prompt many other countries to adopt similar legislation*

Pro-euthanasia activists, who have been campaigning since 1973 for legislation, were in buoyant mood last night, but they remained adamant that the debate had been a long and a fair one.

Dr Rob Jonquiere, director of the country's main pro-euthanasia lobby, said: 'We've been discussing this issue for the past 25 years. It was an open debate and it is good that it took such a long time.

'I think my life is my life. Dying is the only security I have in my life and the majority of the Dutch population agree with me.'

Only 8% of the population is fiercely opposed to euthanasia. 'This is not about asking a doctor to commit a crime but about asking for help.'

Once the formalities are completed – a process expected to take two weeks – doctors will be able to perform euthanasia without fear of prosecution. In the past doctors have found themselves hauled before the courts for performing the practice despite having the full consent of the dying patient.

Under the law, euthanasia will be administered only to patients who are in continuous, unbearable and incurable suffering. A second opinion will be required, the patient must be judged to be of sound mind, and their request to die must be made voluntarily, independently and persistently.

The decision to decriminalise the practice in the Netherlands could prompt many other countries to adopt similar legislation.

Deborah Annetts, of the Voluntary Euthanasia Society in Britain, said: 'It is of major significance to other countries. A psychological barrier has been broken.'

In Belgium a draft law is under consideration and Britain, France, Australia and Italy all have strong euthanasia movements.

The Netherlands showed the rest of Europe the way when it came to tolerating soft drugs and the commercialisation of sex and it has now taken the lead on mercy killing. But a small committed section of the Dutch population will always feel betrayed by the liberal instincts of fellow country-men.

Senator Kars Veling, from the small Christian Union party, said last night: 'I am ashamed of this as a Dutchman. I think it is a terrible mistake.'

How the world legislates

Belgium: A law legalising euthanasia is expected to be approved later this year.

Sweden: 'Suicide assistance' is a non-punishable offence. A doctor can, in extreme cases, unplug life support machines.

Denmark: Terminally ill patients can decide if and when they should abandon vital treatment.

France: Euthanasia is illegal but the law does not regard a doctor's considered decision to refuse life-saving medication as murder.

Britain: Euthanasia is a criminal offence carrying a mandatory life prison sentence. The BMA has always opposed euthanasia, but a minority of doctors would like the law changed.

Germany: Euthanasia is a highly sensitive issue. The administration of a deadly drug is regarded as murder.

America: Euthanasia is outlawed, although Oregon allows medically assisted suicide where a doctor gives a patient lethal drugs but does not administer them.

Australia: Northern Territory passed a law allowing euthanasia in 1996 but it was later repealed by the federal government.

China: The government authorises hospitals to practise euthanasia in the terminal phase of an illness if patients formally request it.

© *Guardian Newspapers Limited 2001*

Man tells radio show how he killed mother

By Martin Wainwright

Detectives and a coroner are investigating a man's tearful claim on a radio phone-in programme that he ended his terminally-ill mother's life after what he took as hints from medical staff.

The caller was traced at the weekend to the address in north Derbyshire from which he rang BBC Radio Sheffield during a discussion on the Dutch government's recent decision to legalise euthanasia.

The station's logbook of call details was surrendered after South Yorkshire police obtained a court order, following a day of discussion between officers and the BBC.

The man was asked by the programme's presenter, Tony Robinson, if he understood that giving details could get him into trouble. He replied that he did, but that ending his mother's 'terrible' suffering was worth facing a possible court case.

Derbyshire police interviewed the man yesterday and said that the case was being handled 'very sensitively', with particular concern for the feelings of the family.

A spokesman said that the coroner of the Hundred of Scarsdale had been informed and was also considering the case.

The man, who gave his name on air as John, described how he had given his dying mother an overdose of liquid morphine four years ago. He detailed his mother's agonising condition – blind, incontinent and no longer able to eat or speak. 'I don't regret it,' he said. 'It was the right thing to do. She was in a terrible state. It wasn't my mother.'

He described how he had turned to a doctor and nurse on a house call and begged them: 'Can't you do anything for her?

'Their eyes both turned to a bottle of liquid morphine which was on the shelf,' he told listeners. 'It was obvious what the implication was.'

Mr Robinson – an experienced and popular broadcaster whose phone-in the previous week on organ donors had prompted a surgeon to ring in from an operating theatre – gently reminded the caller of the implications. But the man said he knew he could be in trouble, but was certain he had done the right thing.

'I suppose I could still face court action but it was worth it,' he said.

Gary Keown, managing editor of Radio Sheffield, said that the interview had been highly emotional and dealt with very difficult circumstances. Police had become involved, he said, after a news agency picked up the broadcast and rang the South Yorkshire force for a comment. The BBC asked that the detectives' request for logbook details be put in writing, which led to the court order.

The investigation is expected to consider details of the morphine dose, which can be a difficult problem in cases of extremely severe pain.

In May last year Newcastle upon Tyne GP David Moor was acquitted of murdering a pensioner patient with morphine, after medical disagreements in court on issues including the risk of death from heavy pain-killing doses.

© *Guardian Newspapers Limited 2000*

Why I killed my mother

A man claimed on a radio phone-in last week that he had given his dying mother a lethal dose of morphine. As the euthanasia debate resurfaces, Elizabeth Summerfield explains why she hastened her terminally ill mother's end

On the morning I decided to kill my mother, time seemed to slow to a halt. A year had sped by in a chaos of emotions, hurtling between hope and despair, love and fear, at disorienting speed. Then came the final diagnosis: terminal cancer, and not long to live. Our world shrank fast as she became increasingly ill and immobile, and time warped as night merged into day and back again, punctuated by long periods of her sleeping silence, pierced by bursts of excruciating, unimaginable pain.

There had been moments of terror for us both, but when I made the decision – that she must die and that I must be the one to do it – I was extremely calm. For days, I had watched her body twitch in agony as the dosage of the painkillers she was given proved inadequate. I had argued and pleaded with the doctors and health visitors responsible for her medication and still she wasn't getting what she needed. I had to do something.

When I did, time passed in slow motion, quietly. There were no great dramatic gestures, no hopes to grasp at, no future to struggle towards … just me and my mum in the bedroom that had become our world. The sun was beginning to shine through the curtains and buses had begun to trundle past her window. I stroked her hair. I tried but probably failed to say how much I loved her. Then I pressed the button that killed her.

I did love her. In the last few years of her life, we had begun to appreciate each other as women, not simply as mother and daughter. Our roles had blurred, our relationship had shifted: I taught her shopping and she taught me sitcoms. We watched too many episodes of *Cheers* together, ate too much chocolate and got drunk on strange bottles lurking in her sideboard. She infuriated me; I exasperated her. And

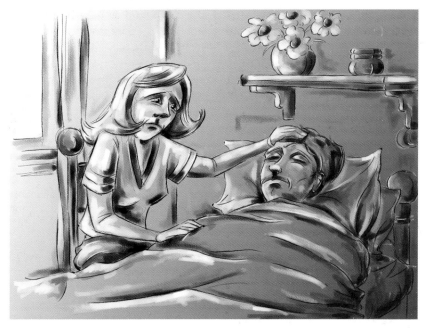

we talked for hours at a time. One night, we discussed what we would do were either of us ever in a position of great suffering and no hope. We agreed to 'pull the plug'.

It took my mum 24 hours to die from the moment I pressed that button. This simple action boosted the flow of the morphine cocktail that was entering her body via the small syringe pump pinned to her nightie. She slid, or, more accurately, was pushed, into a coma from which she never surfaced. I hope that she died painlessly.

> *The need to hasten her death would not have arisen had the doctors in charge of her care had the courage, confidence and training to control her suffering*

But perhaps she did not. I had had to guess the dose that would kill her. A visiting nurse had told me that mum wasn't allowed more than a certain level of drugs because any more would be lethal. So I had taken that figure and doubled it. Her body stopped arching in pain, her moans subsided and the rictus of agony eased. But perhaps, rather than easing my mother's pain and hastening her death, the dosage swept her into a vortex of paralysis, fear and hallucination. I have no way of knowing.

It doesn't help to know that drug-induced terror was nothing new to her. In two different hospitals, as her illness progressed, I had found her hallucinating in silent fear, her fingers locked to the arms of her chair. The few nurses on shift were too busy to notice. When I held her hand, she cried. I complained and was told that her dosage needed 'fine-tuning'; this consisted of dropping it so dramatically that she lay screeching in pain. I was assured that this was not inadequate care but 'how it had to be', this seesawing between dementia and searing pain.

How it had to be? Once diagnosed as terminal, when there was 'nothing more the hospital could do', it was suggested my mother enter a hospice. Within 24 hours, she was virtually pain-free and in control, sitting up laughing at her drug-induced antics the day before. She had her personality, her humour, and what was left of her life, back.

Not once while there was she allowed to flip into drugged terror and never once was she left to suffer. The staff were dedicated, expert, watchful, respectful. They knew the importance of pain control, dignity, individuality and a good shampoo and set. They talked about life, death, children, funerals, fears, social security forms, memories and aroma-therapy. And when people didn't want to talk, they knew how to be silent. Mum rallied so much, she felt well enough to go home to die.

Home was where she belonged and where we both wanted her to be. That was where she wanted to die. But it meant a switch from the care of the hospice into the care of her GP's surgery. Don't worry, we were told, all the doctors were skilled in pain control.

The first doctor to visit was unsure whether my mother's drugs should be administered intravenously or intramuscularly, or how to set up the syringe pump, or how to work out the dose needed over 12 hours. He miscalculated and it ran out at 4am. Then there was the one who was unwilling to give diamorphine at the dose recommended by the hospice because he thought it 'dangerous'. Dangerous to whom?

'Double effect' is the term used to describe the action of pain control drugs that are administered to alleviate suffering but which actually hasten death in the process. It is perfectly legal and, according to recent surveys, supported by the majority of GPs. Just hope to God you get one of those. What is the lay person to do in the middle of the night, faced with a dying relative and a doctor unwilling to help? Perhaps he had ethical objections; perhaps it was misplaced fear of prosecution. Yes, he had a problem. But my mother's was bigger. By then, there were no hospice beds available. The pain had to stop and, two days later, I stopped it.

It is not the fact that I had to kill her that hurts the most. What is still so raw, and so hard to live with, is the

realisation that I need not have killed her, that my well-intentioned but amateurish attempts to give her some dignity in dying were the final acts in a tragic farce.

This was not the mercy-killing of someone whose pain was beyond the reach of medical knowledge, as the headline-hitting cases tend to be. This was the killing of a woman whose pain could have been controlled with commonplace drugs and existing expertise. The need to hasten her death would not have arisen had the doctors in charge of her care had the courage, confidence and training to control her suffering. But they didn't. She was not yet 60, and she deserved better.

After my mother died, a nurse who came to take away the needles and medicines calculated that a quantity of drugs had been used that could not be accounted for. This was serious: Class A drugs were 'missing'. She told me the police could be called.

'You have to do what you have to do,' I said.

'We all have to do that sometimes, don't we?' she replied softly. No more was said.

That you will die is a certainty; how you die, in this country, is a lottery. The quality of palliative care depends largely on where you live, where you are looked after and by whom. The doses of morphine

---

Talk to most people over the age of 30 and they will have a relative or friend who has died in distress or cruel indignity

---

administered for pain relief vary hugely, depending on where the patient is being treated. The levels of attention and respect accorded to the dying range from neglectful indifference to expert dedication.

Even the law cannot promise uniformity of provision and approach. The test case brought by the late, courageous Annie Lindsell before her death from motor neurone disease in 1997 underlined the legality of 'double effect' under English law. However, this does not necessarily mean that the doctor treating your relative or friend will want to administer those drugs, will agree to administer them or even know how to administer them effectively.

The care of the terminally and chronically ill in this country is a mess. Talk to most people over the age of 30 and they will have a relative or friend who has died in distress or cruel indignity. Care of the dying is a specialist skill, too infrequently undertaken by specialists; the needs of the dying are at the bottom of a very large heap of medical priorities, and there they may remain.

No one can ever know how many carers like me attempt, succeed or at least consider the killing of loved ones, but we can be sure we know of only the very tip of a huge iceberg of misery. The numbers affected will rise as life expectancy increases and, with it, the percentage of people looking after elderly relatives. Yet the situation remains ignored because the dead don't shout, the dead don't vote, and those left behind are usually too numb to complain.

Only when more people accept the unpalatable truth that their relative, or even they themselves, could be denied access to adequate pain relief when they are dying, will real changes begin to be made.

I watched my mother suffer in a way that broke her heart and mine. And I killed her. In a society with the means to control the pain that fuels such crude acts of compassion, this seems pathetic and barbaric, yet I felt I had no choice.

It is not a dilemma I wish my own children to face.

Allow these women to die with dignity, beg families

Judge asked to overrule fears of human rights breach

The families and doctors of two women suffering a 'living death' yesterday pleaded for their right to die in dignity.

The patients, aged 36 and 49, were said to be so badly brain-damaged that they are completely unaware of the outside world.

Those closest to them have asked for life support to be withdrawn, but fear that European human rights legislation introduced on Monday would make this tantamount to murder.

Since the 1993 case of Tony Bland, a brain-damaged Hillsborough survivor, it had been established under common law that doctors can allow a patient to die where it is held to be in the patient's best interests.

But according to Article 2 of the controversial new law, everybody has the 'right to life' and medical staff fear prosecution if they stop feeding or treating people who are in a so-called persistent vegetative state (PVS).

Yesterday Dame Elizabeth Butler-Sloss, Britain's leading woman judge and President of the High Court Family Division, heard the case of the two women – both diagnosed as being in a PVS – at London's High Court.

John Grace QC, representing the two hospital trusts treating the women in the north of England, said that both families backed the application to withdraw life support. He said: 'No amount of rhetoric as to the law should obscure the tragedies behind these cases.

'Expert independent witnesses agree they are undoubtedly cases of PVS, described as a twilight zone of suspended animation where death commences whilst life continues. They are suffering a living death.'

The women and the hospitals cannot be named for legal reasons.

By Peter Allen

Mrs M, who is 49, was left severely brain-damaged by an anaesthetic accident during a gynaecological operation abroad in 1997.

She was brought back to Britain by her husband where four doctors agreed she was a PVS case.

> **'One of the relatives has said that she was someone who was full of life and she would not want to live as she is now'**

Although she responds to some stimuli, doctors agree that these are reflex actions and that there is no possibility of recovery.

Mr Grace said doctors had estimated that if life support continues, Mrs M could live for a further 12 years or even longer.

He said that the second woman, Ms H, was now 36 and had suffered from severe epilepsy for most of her life, requiring medication to control her seizures.

'Despite her condition she is described by everyone as having been a lively and bubbly personality.'

Mr Grace said Ms H was on holiday in the US at about Christmas last year when she suffered

pancreatitis as a result of her medication.

She was brought back to this country by air ambulance and admitted to hospital on January 16. On January 18 she suffered a cardiac arrest and had been in a vegetative state since.

Mr Grace told the judge that nutrition had been a constant problem in Ms H's case and since September 23 it had not been possible to administer any to her.

She was, however, still receiving drugs when necessary and hydration. The judge said that because of the circumstances of Ms H's case she was concerned that everyone should know as quickly as possible what was to happen.

If doctors withdraw feeding and hydration, she would die within five to 14 days without distress.

'One of the relatives has said that she was someone who was full of life and she would not want to live as she is now,' said Mr Grace.

He said that both the patients were the 'victims of medical technology that did not exist when the European Convention of Human Rights was formulated in 1950.

'In these circumstances, withdrawal or non-reinstitution of life-sustaining treatment would not be unlawful,' he added, confirming that he would be relying on the Lords decision in the Bland case.

Despite fears to the contrary, Mr Grace believed that there would be no conflict between the principles established in the Bland case and the new Human Rights Act.

He said this was accepted by Ben Emmerson QC, who is representing the patients through the Official Solicitor, Laurence Oates.

The case was adjourned.

'We can have a choice about dying –

but not the Dutch way'

By Catherine Pepinster

I watched my grandmother die some years ago; a lingering death caused by cancer which first attacked her throat and then her brain.

Seeing a once vivacious woman become first an angry, then a paranoid and later a mute and passive creature was almost unbearable. Would it not have been more merciful if a doctor had filled a syringe and injected her with a lethal drug, quietly letting her slip away from us when she was not yet in the darkest days of her disease?

Such an end will soon be possible in the Netherlands. Last week it became the first country in the world to legalise euthanasia. Dutch doctors already perform euthanasia on 3,000 patients a year, but this latest Bill is supposed to bring the practice into the open; once it is approved by the Dutch Senate in the spring (which is highly likely) a doctor will be required to ensure that the patient's request is voluntary, based on full information, and is carefully considered. The patient's condition must be unbearable and untreatable, and a second medical opinion must corroborate the first physician's.

No other country has such a law, yet there is a growing acceptance of euthanasia across the world. It is tolerated in Belgium, Switzerland and Colombia, as it has been in the Netherlands for years. In the US, Oregon allows doctor-assisted suicide for the terminally ill. Australia's Northern Territory legalised it in 1996 but repealed it a year later. An idea once taboo – that killing people deliberately is acceptable, desirable even – is becoming tolerated. Of course, we have always had exceptions: we kill people in wars, in self-defence. But ever since Hippocrates, doctors have been supposed to save lives, not cause deaths.

Medical advances have changed that. Doctors today are often not so much saving lives as prolonging them. What made the condition of my grandmother so dreadful was not that she was suffering from a fatal illness but that she became a victim of scientific and medical progress. The treatment that was available kept her alive long after the quality of her life had been destroyed. Is it any wonder that people seek drastic solutions, if the very professionals whom we want to ease suffering instead extend it.

That solution can make a patient feel in control again. We don't expect others to decide whom we marry, when or whether we have children, where we live. Why should it be down to the whim of nature to decide when we die? Isn't death the most significant moment of our life, and should we not have the right to decide when it comes? It should not be down to the bogus notion of letting nature takes it course. What is natural is what we're used to. It seems perfectly natural for us to have somebody else's blood transfused into our veins, for example, because that has been possible for generations. We don't say to the elderly person who has difficulty walking that that's nature taking its course; we expect them to be able to get an artificial hip.

In this way, deciding about one's dying seems a matter of private morality; it is part of our 'moral sense' about how we ought to live. It is as

Public opinion on euthanasia

Question: 'Some adults say that the law should allow adults to receive medical help to an immediate peaceful death if they suffer from an incurable physical illness that is intolerable to them, provided they have previously requested such help in writing. Please tell me whether you agree or disagree with this?' Around 2,000 interviews carried out each time (adults 15+). The results were as follows:

Legend: For / Against / Undecided

%	1976	1985	1989	1993
For	69%	72%	75%	79%
Against	17%	21%	16%	10%
Undecided	14%	8%	9%	11%

Ed. Jowell R. et al *British Social Attiudes: the 13th Report,* Social and Community Planning Research 1996 (published by Dartmouth, ISBN 1-85521-607-8)

Source: Voluntary Euthanasia Society

much a part of the way I perceive the world as whether I think I should lie when it suits me, or whether it is shaming to deceive somebody. But euthanasia is not just a private issue. Deciding to legalise it is a public statement about the kind of society we are. It would certainly make us more honest: for years doctors in this country have carried out a form of passive euthanasia, by treating patients with drugs that provide pain relief. If a dose is high enough, there is a risk that the patient will die, and often does.

But intentional killing is a very different matter. The Netherlands' change in the law is supposed to protect doctors, yet making euthanasia legal may well place an enormous burden on them to provide this service. Patients too may be placed under undue pressure from relatives to choose death as a way out, a solution to their ills.

When I waited for my grandmother to die, the way she was dealt

with by the health service was the most distressing experience of all. She was moved from one hospital to another. Sometimes she was placed in a ward with patients who were not suffering from a terminal illness, as she was, but were suffering from acute dementia. What my grandmother needed was not a grim hospital where the emphasis was on treatment, but a place where the priority was care; a place where people accepted that she would die but did all that was possible to make her final days as comfortable and pain-free as possible. She needed a hospice. In the Netherlands, where hospices are

almost unknown, that would not even have been an option.

However much we talk about mercy and dignity, euthanasia is still a form of killing. But what matters when people kill – and our acceptance of killing in war and in self-defence makes this clear – is motive. The doctor's aim in killing his patient should be carefully examined. The House of Lords select committee on medical ethics unanimously agreed that there should be no change in the law on euthanasia. It was right. But to impose a mandatory life sentence on a doctor is too harsh. We should not go down the Dutch road; but if such a case of deliberate killing came to court, a judge should consider whether the doctor did indeed act in the best interests of the patient and on a persistent request. Then it should be open to the judge to offer a lenient sentence – or none at all.

Glossary of terms

The following terms may be used in discussions about end-of-life decision making

Advance directives: A general term that describes two kinds of legal documents, living wills and medical powers of attorney. These documents allow you to give instructions about future medical care and appoint a person to make health care decisions if you are unable to make them yourself. Each state regulates the use of advance directives differently.

Benefits and burdens: A commonly used guideline for deciding whether or not to withhold or withdraw medical treatments. A benefit can refer to the successful outcome of a medical procedure or treatment. Outcomes can be medical (e.g. the heart beats again) or functional (e.g. the person is able to walk to the bathroom after being incapacitated by a stroke), or support the patient's values (for example, the patient is able to die at home as he wished).

However, a benefit from one point of view can be experienced as

a burden from another and might be viewed differently by doctors, patients and families. For example, if a patient is resuscitated and the heart starts beating again, this is a successful outcome from a medical point of view and a doctor may consider it a benefit. To the patient who is dying from a serious illness or disease, resuscitation may cause further injury and only contribute to the overall experience of suffering. This success, from the doctor's point of view, might actually be experienced as an additional burden by the patient. Discussions of the benefits and burdens of medical treatments should occur within the framework of the patient's overall goals for care.

Best interest: In the context of refusal of medical treatment or end-of-life court opinions, a standard for making health care decisions based on what others believe to be 'best' for a patient by weighing the benefits and the

burdens of continuing, withholding or withdrawing treatment. (Contrast with 'substituted judgment'.)

Brain death: The irreversible loss of all brain function. Most states legally define death to include brain death.

Capacity: In the health care context, the ability of the patient to understand and appreciate the nature and consequences of health care decisions and to make an informed decision. The term competent is also used to indicate ability to make informed decisions.

Case law: Law made by court cases rather than legislation.

Clear and convincing evidence: A high measure or degree of proof that may be required legally to prove a patient's wishes. A few states require clear and convincing evidence that an incompetent patient would want to refuse life-support before treatment may be stopped unless the patient has completed an advance directive authorised by the state's law.

Constitutional law: Law based on either federal or state constitutions. Generally, it concerns the fundamental principles that regulate the relation between the government and its citizens. The United States Supreme Court has ultimate authority to interpret the US Constitution and decide the constitutionality of a law.

Do-not-resuscitate (DNR) order: A DNR order is a physician's written order instructing health care providers not to attempt cardiopulmonary resuscitation (CPR) in case of cardiac or respiratory arrest. A person with a valid DNR order will not be given CPR under these circumstances. Although the DNR order is written at the request of a person or his or her family, it must be signed by a physician to be valid.

Double effect: According to the ethical principle known as the 'rule of double effect', effects that would be morally wrong if caused intentionally are permissible if foreseen but unintended. An example is the administration of pain medication with the intention of relieving pain and with the possible unintended secondary effect of hastening death.

Euthanasia: The term traditionally has been used to refer to the hastening of a suffering person's death or 'mercy killing'. Voluntary active euthanasia involves an intervention requested by a competent individual that is administered to that person to cause death, for example, if a physician gives a lethal injection with the patient's full informed consent. Involuntary or non-voluntary active euthanasia involves a physician engaging in an act to end a patient's life without that patient's full informed consent.

Guardian ad litem: Someone appointed by the court to represent the interests of a minor or incompetent person in a legal proceeding.

Incompetent: See 'Capacity'.

Hospice care: A programme to deliver palliative care to individuals who are in the final stages of terminal illness. In addition to providing palliative care and personal support to the patient, hospice includes support for the patient's family while the patient is dying, and bereavement support.

Legislation: Laws enacted by state or federal representatives.

Life-sustaining Treatment: Treatments (medical procedures) that replace or support an essential bodily function (may also be called life-support treatments). Life-sustaining treatments include cardiopulmonary resuscitation, mechanical ventilation, artificial nutrition and hydration, dialysis, and certain other treatments.

Living will: A type of advance directive in which an individual documents his or her wishes about future medical treatment if he or she is at the end of life and unable to communicate. It may also be called a 'directive to physicians', 'health care declaration', or 'medical directive.' The purpose of a living will is to guide family members and doctors in deciding how aggressively to use medical treatments to delay death.

Medical power of attorney: A document that allows an individual to appoint someone else to make decisions about his or her medical care if he or she is unable to communicate. It may also be called a health care proxy, durable power of attorney for health care, or appointment of a health care agent or surrogate. The person appointed may be called a health care agent, surrogate, attorney-in-fact, or proxy.

Palliative care: A comprehensive approach to treating serious illness that focuses on the physical, psychological, spiritual, and existential needs of the patient. Its goal is to achieve the best quality of life available to the patient by relieving suffering, controlling pain and symptoms, and enabling the patient to achieve maximum functional capacity. Respect for the patient's culture, beliefs, and values is an essential component. Palliative care is sometimes called 'comfort care' or 'hospice-type care'. (Contrast with 'best interests'.)

Physician-hastened death (sometimes referred to as physician-assisted suicide): A physician supplies the means, usually a prescription for a lethal dose of medication, which a terminally ill individual can use to end their own life.

Substituted judgment: The doctrine of substituted judgment permits an individual to make medical decisions for a patient when the patient is unable to communicate. The decision maker must make the decision the patient would have made under those circumstances. The decision maker is not permitted to choose what he or she thinks is best for the patient, rather what the patient would have chosen.

Surrogate decision-making laws: Refers to laws that allow an individual or group of individuals to make decisions about medical treatments for a patient who has lost decision-making capacity and did not prepare an advance directive.

Withholding or withdrawing treatment: Forgoing life-sustaining measures or discontinuing them after they have been used for a certain period of time.

• The above information is from the Partnership for Caring web site which can be found at www.partnershipforcaring.org. Questions or comments regarding this web site may be directed to pfc@partnershipforcaring.org

Dutch MPs back euthanasia law

But Dutch public are bitterly divided

By Joan Clements in The Hague

Holland became the first democratic country to legalise euthanasia yesterday when Dutch MPs voted by more than two to one to allow doctors to help patients to die under strict conditions.

Although the practice has been tolerated for more than two decades – and more than 2,000 people each year have been killed on request – doctors have always risked criminal prosecution for murder unless they followed certain guidelines.

The decision polarised opinion in the country, with opponents of euthanasia, especially in the Calvinist churches and hospice movement, fearing the new law will open the floodgates to thousands more deaths. One critic said: 'In the Netherlands your life is no longer safe.'

Yesterday's 104-40 decision by the Dutch parliament's lower house has to be ratified next year by the upper house. But this is regarded as a formality. Holland is unique in its readiness to countenance euthanasia. There was a brief period four years ago in Australia's Northern Territory when physician-assisted suicide was allowed but the law was repealed the following year.

The Dutch experience dates to the early Eighties when the Supreme Court held that a doctor who in certain circumstances killed a patient could successfully invoke the defence of necessity to justify his action.

Euthanasia remained in theory illegal, though no doctor was ever successfully prosecuted for murder. Many doctors, fearful of facing murder charges, backed the new Bill. Other supporters said it championed the rights of patients and brought a long-standing practice into the open. Thom DeGraaf, parliamentary leader of the Liberal D'66 party, said: 'This is for people who are in great pain and have no prospect for recovery.'

But smaller parties in the parliament were appalled. One MP said: 'This will certainly open the floodgates. How can individual cases be controlled? What about family pressure? Would this not be an easy way to get rid of ailing relatives because nursing them has become too much trouble?'

Religious groups drew parallels with Nazi Germany. 'The same line of reasoning is being used as in Germany in 1935 . . . In the Netherlands your life is no longer safe,' said Bert Dorenbos, of the Scream for Life organisation.

An opinion poll two years ago showed support from 50 per cent of the population, with the remainder either opposed or undecided. Under the new law, euthanasia may be carried out only if an adult patient makes a voluntary, well-considered and lasting request to die and faces a future of continuous and unbearable suffering.

The doctor must inform the patient about his or her prospects and reach the firm conclusion that there is no reasonable alternative. A second physician must be consulted and life must be ended in a 'medically appropriate' way.

A Vatican spokesman, Joaquin Navarro Valls, said it was regretted that Holland had become 'the first country to adopt legislation that divides legislators and public opinion, a law that violates the dignity of human beings'.

Medical debate

Doctors are split over legalising euthanasia

A dispute between two royal medical colleges over a report on euthanasia has highlighted deep divisions among doctors over whether they should help end the lives of terminally ill patients.

The Royal College of General Practitioners has refused to endorse a 'position statement' on medical treatment at the end of life, produced by the Royal College of Physicians, because it failed to 'break new ground'.

Euthanasia is a subject of intense debate within the medical profession because of the growing recognition of the need to respect patients' wishes, set against the increasing potential to maintain life. Surveys show increasing public support in Britain for euthanasia, which is already legal in the Netherlands and the US state of Oregon.

The two colleges set up a joint working party on the subject in 1998 with a radical remit to 'identify the kinds of conduct which constitute euthanasia and advise how far they could be justified on moral grounds'.

The idea came from Professor Sir George Alberti, the president of the Royal College of Physicians, who was keen to challenge the prevailing orthodoxy that euthanasia was wrong under all circumstances. The aim was to start a public debate.

But after three years, the 19-strong group produced a statement of just two pages affirming its support for the status quo. The statement says that treatments which may shorten a patient's life can be accepted if the intention is to relieve suffering, but that medical acts which have the

By Jeremy Laurance,
Health Editor

clear intention of ending a patient's life cannot be justified.

Publication of the statement in the *Journal of the Royal College of Physicians* last month was

> *Euthanasia is a subject of intense debate within the medical profession because of the growing recognition of the need to respect patients' wishes*

accompanied by a note which read: 'This position statement was . . . received but not endorsed by the Royal College of General Practitioners.'

Professor Michael Pringle, president of the Royal College of GPs, said: 'We felt it was repetitious and did not break new ground.' He added: 'We are seeing the liberalisation of social norms that will inevitably lead to a rethinking on this issue in another five years. By then we may have come to a position where we can accept that some people have the right to choose in the terminal stages of their life not to prolong it. But equally the pendulum may have swung back.'

Professor Ian Gilmore, the registrar of the Royal College of Physicians, said: 'You could say we chickened out of the big questions.' The group's statement went through a number of drafts and at one stage omitted reference to the consent of the patient. Dr Iona Heath, a north London GP and representative of the Royal College of GPs on the group, said: 'The whole thing was a bit of a catastrophe. It did nothing to provide what people wanted, which was more of a debate.'

But Sir Stephen Tumim, the former chief inspector of prisons appointed to chair the working party, had no appetite for a debate. After a year the group agreed to focus on how to provide 'sound and compassionate treatment at the end of life'. They say voluntary euthanasia is widely believed to occur in the UK.

© 2001 The Independent Newspaper (UK) Ltd

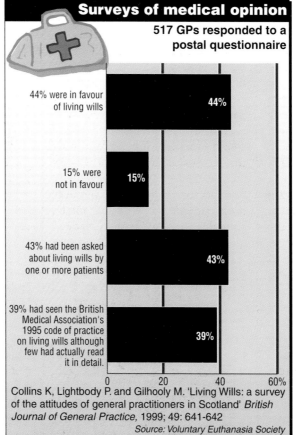

Surveys of medical opinion

517 GPs responded to a postal questionnaire

44% were in favour of living wills — 44%

15% were not in favour — 15%

43% had been asked about living wills by one or more patients — 43%

39% had seen the British Medical Association's 1995 code of practice on living wills although few had actually read it in detail. — 39%

0   20   40   60%

Collins K, Lightbody P. and Gilhooly M. 'Living Wills: a survey of the attitudes of general practitioners in Scotland' *British Journal of General Practice*, 1999; 49: 641-642

Source: Voluntary Euthanasia Society

First do no harm

Doctors opposing euthanasia

The aim of 'First Do No Harm' is to bring together doctors who are opposed to the current campaign for euthanasia, and to exchange information.

The Universal Declaration of Human Rights states in Article 3: 'Everyone has the right to life, liberty and security of person.' When the right to life depends on 'quality', no patient is safe.

Dr Karel Gunning, World President of the Doctors' Federation, said in London: 'Once we accept killing a patient as a solution for one problem, we will find hundreds of situations where killing seems to be the solution.'[1] In Holland 10,000 people carry 'Don't kill me' papers – so-called 'euthanasia passports'.

In Britain the Bland judgment in 1993 defined food and water as 'medical treatment' if given through a tube, which allowed them to be withdrawn.[2] A Dept of Health spokesman said this judgment 'pointed the way forward'.[3]

The BMA's 1998 consultation paper discussed withholding fluids from victims of a stroke.[4] It is constantly argued that advance refusals of treatment should be made legally binding. Penalties have been proposed, in draft legislation, for any doctor who would not pass on a patient to a colleague willing to cause death by dehydration, if he objected to doing it himself.[5]

Dr Helga Kuhse, a leading campaigner for euthanasia, said in 1984: 'If we can get people to accept the removal of all treatment and care – especially the removal of food and fluids – they will see what a painful way this is to die and then, in the patient's best interest, they will accept the lethal injection.'[6]

In the first case involving patients in 'PVS' since the Human Rights Act 1998 came into force, the chairman of the Family Division of the High Court granted leave to two Hospital Trusts to discontinue 'artificial' hydration, ruling that Article 2 of the European Convention, 'Everyone's right to life shall be protected by law' did not apply to such patients. Article 3, forbidding inhuman and degrading treatment, did not protect them either, since they were 'insensate'.[7]

An opinion poll in 1987 showed that if euthanasia were legalised, one-third of the British public would expect all geriatricians to be required to carry it out, as part of their contract.[8]

In the Scottish Parliament the Adult with Incapacity (Scotland) Bill was passed in March 2000 without the amendments which would have protected adults with incapacity from having their death brought about or hastened.[9] The Lord Chancellor has stated that he intends to introduce a similar Bill in England as soon as parliamentary time allows.[10]

If doctors become killers, patients become afraid to go into hospital. Against allegations that hospice doctors are killing their patients already, Drs Nigel Sykes and Fiona Randall have pointed out: 'Experience gained in palliative care has shows that morphine, used in a carefully balanced way to counteract pain, doesn't accelerate death'.[11] Studies in the USA confirm this.[12] Death is achieved in Holland with the aid of curare to paralyse the lungs and heart.[13]

Doctors have the power over their patients, which must not be abused. ' . . . The German medical community set its own course in 1933. In some respects this course even outpaced the new government, which had rein in the profession's eager pursuit of enforced eugenic sterilisations.'[14]

Doctors who disagreed with euthanasia and eugenic policies were silent then.

Doctors in Britain should not be silent now.

References
1. Meeting of the European Doctors Union, Moses Room, House of Lords, 25 March 1997.
2. *Airedale National Health Service Trust v. Bland* 1993.
3. *BMJ* 1993; 306; 1150.
4. *Withdrawing and Withholding Treatment* (Consultation Paper), London, BMA, 1998.
5. Medical Treatment (Advance Directives) Bill (Section 8), February 1992, prepared by the All Party Voluntary Euthanasia Group.
6. Fifth Biennial Congress of Societies for the Right to Die, held in Nice, Sept. 1984.
7. *Values and Attitudes in an Ageing Society* 1998 interim report, part of the 'Millennium Debate of the Age', co-ordinated by Age Concern.
8. MORI poll (1808 respondents) fieldwork 4-7 December 1987, published by the Doctors' Federation.
9. *Daily Mail* 28 July 1997.
10. *J. Clin Oncol* 1992 Jan; 10(1): 149-55 JAMA, 1992 Feb 19; 267(7): 949-953.
11. *Medical Decisions at the End of Life*, The Hague, Ministry of Justice, 1991; 11: 52.
12. *BMJ* 1996; 313:1453.
13. *Medical Decisions at the End of Life*, The Hague, Ministry of Justice, 1991; II: 52.
14. *BMJ* 1996; 313: 1453

• The above information is an extract from First Do No Harm's web site which can be found at www.donoharm.org.uk

© *First Do No Harm*

Trust me, I'm a doctor . . .

Dr Bert Keizer debates the ethical and human issues with Dr Anthony Daniels, a British doctor strenuously opposed to the legalisation of euthanasia

Last week, the Netherlands became the first country in the world to legalise euthanasia. A Bill passed by the Dutch parliament now allows doctors to end the lives of patients who are considered to be suffering 'unbearably and without hope' – formally recognising a practice accepted there for 30 years.

Dr Bert Keizer, a geriatrician at the Devreugdehof nursing home in Amsterdam and author of *Dancing with Mister D: Notes on Life and Death* – a novel that describes physician-assisted death in graphic detail – acknowledges that he has been involved in the practice for years and admits to once admin-istering a fatal injection.

Here he debates the ethical and human issues with Dr Anthony Daniels, a British doctor strenuously opposed to the legalisation of euthanasia.

Dr Daniels: There are, for me, several objections to euthanasia. First and foremost, that it breaks an immemorial moral injunction against killing, one that, in the Hippocratic tradition, is doubly powerful for doctors.

The second is that voluntary euthanasia stands at the top of a very slippery slope. Already in Holland a depressed woman has been helped to die by her doctor, as has a young woman with anorexia nervosa. Many patients who did not ask to die have been killed by their doctors, who considered that they would be better off dead. Guidelines laid down for euthanasia have already been disregarded on very many occasions, proving that the slippery slope is a real one.

Euthanasia breaks an immemorial moral injunction against killing, one that, in the Hippocratic tradition, is doubly powerful for doctors

---

Third, the desire to die is itself open to manipulation. It can be either promoted or discouraged by the treatment that people receive at the hands of their relatives, medical carers and the state. Bioethicists are already talking of a patient's duty to die, and, in a climate in which a crass utilitarianism is being imposed on doctors, a weakening of the prohibition on killing would be disastrous.

Dr Keizer: I will address your three points, but first let me define the concept of euthanasia as it is now allowed in Holland. Here it is physician-assisted suicide, in cases where patients are suffering unbearably from a disease from which they cannot recover. The request for such a form of doctor's help must be well considered, not uttered in a whim, nor in the course of a psychiatric disturbance in the sense of a depression.

The doctor must call in a second opinion from a colleague who is not in any way involved in the case, the proceedings must be documented and, after the patient dies, the cause of death must be truthfully reported to the coroner. The entire procedure must be carried out in the pharmaco-logical sense, so there is no messing about with insulin or potassium chloride or even high dosages of morphine.

You speak of the Hippocratic injunction against killing – but there is no killing involved on the doctor's part: it is the patient who takes the overdose.

In response to your second point about the depressed patient and the anorexic girl, I have heard about them and they are almost ritually trotted out in this context. It would be silly for me to say that euthanasia never goes wrong. I can only add that, as against these two staple examples, I could cite hundreds if not thousands of cases where death

PAIN RELIEF?

LIFE RELIEF?

is withheld, to the severe detriment of patients asking for it.

As to doctors killing patients against their wish: please do not just say this in a flippant manner. Give me the addresses of the hospitals where these murders occur and I will see to it that they are brought to justice.

That a procedure is sometimes abused is not a reason for abandoning it. If that were the case, hysterectomies ought to have been stopped long ago, on the basis of the unsettling statistic that the number of hysterectomies increases with the number of gynaecologists, and not with the number of diseased uteri.

Third, yes, the guidelines laid down for euthanasia are often ignored. In Britain, however, there are no guidelines, but believe me it is being performed. Regrettably, government surveys indicate that the number of cases duly reported in Holland is only 40 to 50 per cent. But I hasten to add that, in Britain, the number of reported cases is zero! And that, I'm afraid, is far from the truth. I would feel very uncomfortable with this silence if I were a patient, or a doctor for that matter.

Dr Daniels: The definition of permissible euthanasia in Holland is all very well, but you state in your own book that you yourself have injected people fatally. This is not suicide: it is killing. Even the definition as you give it is the beginning of the slippery slope: could not schizophrenia be considered a disease from which there is no hope of recovery and which causes unbearable suffering?

Whether a disease is unbearable is not just a question of physiology and pathology. It is in large part a question of proper terminal care and of the social and psychological circumstances of the patient. For safeguards to be meaningful and effective, they would have to involve lengthy investigations of the patient's psyche, his family dynamics and the financial implications of his death, among other things. In my experience, second opinions are often rubber stamps.

By your own admission, reporting to the coroner in cases of euthanasia is only 50 per cent. Why

should this be so if there is nothing to hide? This is all the more alarming because there were no serious legal consequences for Dr Chabot, the psychiatrist who helped his depressed patient to die, after he was brought to court. Doctors, it seems, have very little to fear from Dutch courts.

The Dutch government's 1991 Remmelink report suggested that 4,941 patients who had not asked for euthanasia had been killed by their doctors. The comparison of euthanasia with hysterectomy, under the rubric of medical procedure, goes to show how far down the slippery slope we have already gone. We should not forget that gassing people in Nazi Germany was known as 'special treatment'.

You speak of the Hippocratic injunction against killing – but there is no killing involved on the doctor's part: it is the patient who takes the overdose

---

In Britain, the legal guidelines could not be clearer. Euthanasia is against the law.

Dr Keizer: My dear colleague, please don't throw the book at me. It was not journalism, but meant as literature.

That, however, does not alter the fact that, yes, I once injected a patient, and death ensued. I would still maintain that I did not kill the man, because I acted as he begged me to act. I was a young doctor then, and in juvenile over-dedication would have carried him to the grave myself. I now, when involved in euthanasia, insist on patients administering the overdose themselves.

Proper terminal care has not been shown to be effective in eliminating all requests for euthanasia. It is vital in this context to realise that people do not ask for death because of physical pain, but because of their desire to forestall a further physical decline, resulting in a loss of dignity. All of these are

hopelessly subjective criteria, yet we have to bring them into our considerations, because we are talking of suffering people, not of faltering machines.

Considering the practice of palliative care, let me say this: I would rather die in the care of a doctor who is against euthanasia, but who knows how to look after a dying person and puts his best energy into that care, than I would in the care of a doctor who is all for euthanasia, but wholly ignorant of palliative procedures.

Yes, only 50 per cent of cases are being duly reported in Holland. But I repeat: in Italy, Germany, Switzerland, France, Britain, Ireland and most of the United States, the number is zero. This is a joke, for we know it is being done there as well.

As for Remmelink's infamous 4,941 patients who had not asked for euthanasia and had been killed by their doctors – if you are here on the trail of a mass-murder, then please act accordingly. I don't believe for a minute that you seriously believe that your Dutch colleagues are killing patients in the thousands. If you do seriously believe this, then there is a lot more than the North Sea between us.

Let me explain this presumed carnage. Dutch doctors were asked in how many cases they thought it likely that the morphine they gave to their patients might have hastened their deaths. If you change 'hastened' into 'caused', then Dutch genocide is a fact. Do remember, though, that on this count virtually all deaths occurring in British hospices, where the morphine is practically raining down from the ceilings (and God bless them for it), are cases of patients being killed by doctors.

Now that I mention the hallowed hospice movement, it strikes me how we both fall into the trap of trying to be all-knowing about the situation in each other's country. In fact, it is highly unlikely that I, though I once lived in England, would have a clear view of how things stand there, particularly in this delicate area of dying and death.

You are presumptuous in like manner when you state: second opinions are often rubber stamps. But my dear Anthony, you've never been involved in a case of physician-assisted suicide, so where did you find this wisdom?

Finally, Anthony, relax a little, don't be so rigid, you cannot be all right, I cannot be all wrong. If Europe is ever going to mean anything, let us unwind a little.

Dr Daniels: I'm sorry if I sound earnest and humourless. It seems that the terms of our debate have narrowed somewhat. You seem to agree that it is wrong for doctors themselves to give fatal injections. This is what most people in this country think of as euthanasia.

You are quite right, of course, that not all suffering can be avoided by even the best palliative care, but much can, and hard cases make bad law. And perhaps I should explain why any loosening of the law in this country would be particularly dangerous.

Ever since I first qualified as a doctor, more than a quarter of a century ago, there has been a shortage of hospital beds in Britain. Patients wait months for hospital appointments to see specialists, they wait years for their operations, and they wait hours on trolleys in hospital corridors when they are admitted for emergencies.

Meanwhile, elderly patients occupy hospital beds for lack of money to send them anywhere else. There is a shortage of doctors in many specialities, including in terminal care. There would be a temptation to use a short cut to ease the situation, and no doubt utilitarian philosophers could be found to justify it. Since both our political parties are obsessed with getting the best value for money, our Government might even lay down targets for doctors to reach!

While you are probably right that some British doctors practise euthanasia, I don't personally know any who do. For myself, I remain in favour of improving the conditions in which people die, rather than opening Pandora's box.

Dr Keizer: Sounding earnest is fine with me, but I feel that you know what I mean: it is much more fruitful for us as doctors to communicate our doubts about euthanasia than to maul each other with certainties.

The conditions you describe as now pertaining in British hospitals are shocking. Though the Dutch situation is far from ideal (we, too, cope badly with the elderly in general hospitals), things here are not quite as harrowing as in Britain. Still, reflections about the awfulness of the situation in British healthcare should not lead to a dismissal of the Dutch euthanasia policy.

That policy, for what it is worth, deserves to be weighed on its own merits, and, believe me, we have plenty of doubts ourselves. Don't forget that we have gone through a public debate lasting almost 30 years before legislation was enacted.

Finally, I hope not to have committed a typical Dutch error in our exchange: there is a fatal sense of mission to the world that at times seizes some of my compatriots. As to export products, I think we should stick to cheese and hang on to euthanasia for internal use. Meanwhile, anyone is welcome to come and take a look.

'Do no harm' abandoned in Holland

Information from Canadian Physicians for Life

Promoting premature death is no solution to disability, suffering, ageing, and rising health costs. By legalising euthanasia, the Netherlands is going against the Hippocratic tradition in medicine of 'Do No Harm'. Canadian Physicians for Life submits that once a law embarks upon comparing the relative worth of human lives, under whatever guise, it rejects any commitment to protect the inherent dignity of all persons and absorbs into itself a principle which will only result in the abuse and killing of the most vulnerable in society.

According to CPL President, Dr Robert Pankratz, 'In Canada, good palliative care seeks to aggressively relieve the symptoms of a person's suffering without needing to confuse the issue by deciding whether that person deserves death. Ensuring quality palliative care and keeping euthanasia illegal protects the vulnerable from self and their doctor. People need good care, not doctors playing God – they aren't qualified for the job.'

Palliative care physician Dr Margaret Cottle adds, 'Hippocrates knew that killing patients is wrong and leads to abuse. The Netherlands is going against almost 2500 years of societal wisdom.'

The Dutch Health Minister states that their law has 'careful supervisory provisions'. Some Canadians believe euthanasia should be available in special cases only – with strict safeguards in place. But it is clear from the Dutch experience that safeguards do not work. The Netherlands has gone from euthanasia for terminal illness to chronic illness to psychological distress to no illness at all. A doctor in Holland was recently acquitted for killing an elderly man who was 'tired of life' but had no physical or mental illness.

Palliative care physician Dr Margaret Cottle questions, 'Who would provide these so-called safeguards – i.e. laws? The government seems the only viable possibility to most citizens. Ergo. . . the folks who brought us Canada Post and Revenue Canada would be administering and enforcing the regulations which may determine if we live or die. This thought should be sobering.'

Canadians want to invest in high quality palliative care, not the uncontrollable and cheap methods of euthanasia.

• The above information is an extract from Canadian Physicians for Life's web site which can be found at www.physiciansforlife.ca

End of life decisions

Views of the BMA

Euthanasia

The British Medical Association opposes the legalisation of euthanasia or physician-assisted suicide, regarding such measures as in tension with the fundamental role of doctors. The following resolution was passed at the BMA Annual Representatives' Meeting in June 1997: That this Meeting recognises that there is a wide spectrum of views about the issues of physician-assisted suicide and euthanasia and strongly opposes any change in law for the time being.

The BMA recognises that some doctors, having exhausted all other possibilities for ensuring a patient's comfort, may see the deliberate termination of life as the only solution in an individual case. Nevertheless, the BMA maintains that in such circumstances, the doctor should be accountable to the law and to the General Medical Council and be obliged to defend such an action. Basically, the BMA's view is similar to that expressed by the House of Lords Select Committee on Medical Ethics, established in the wake of the Bland case to examine the ethical, legal and clinical implications involved in end of life decisions. In their report,[1] the Committee referred to moving representations it had received from people who wanted euthanasia themselves or who had witnessed

relatives dying in a distressing way. It recognised that every person hopes for an easy death, without suffering or dementia or dependence. The Lords concluded, however, with two comments that are germane to the BMA's position.

The first concerns protection of vulnerable people.

'Ultimately we do not believe that the arguments are sufficient reason to weaken society's prohibition of intentional killing. That prohibition is the cornerstone of law and of social relationships. It protects each one of us impartially, embodying the belief that all are equal. We do not wish that protection to be diminished. We acknowledge that there are individual cases in which euthanasia may be seen by some to be appropriate. But individual cases cannot reasonably establish the foundation of a policy which would have such serious and widespread repercussions. Dying is not only a personal or individual affair. The death of a person affects the lives of others, often in ways and to an extent

which cannot be foreseen. We believe that the issue of euthanasia is one in which the interest of the individual cannot be separated from the interest of society as a whole.'

In fact, the Lords concluded that the interests of society must overrule those of individuals. They thought that if euthanasia were allowed, the elderly, the lonely and the sick would feel pressured to request it.

The Lords' second conclusion was based on practical considerations.

'We do not think it possible to set secure limits on voluntary euthanasia. Some witnesses told us that to legalise voluntary euthanasia was a discrete step which need have no other consequences. But issues of life and death do not lend themselves to clear definition, and without that it would not be possible to frame adequate safeguards against non-voluntary euthanasia if voluntary euthanasia were to be legalised. It would be next to impossible to ensure that all acts of euthanasia were truly voluntary and that any liberalisation of the law was not abused.'

The BMA maintains that, if doctors were authorised to carry out euthanasia or assisted suicide, however carefully circumscribed the situation, they would acquire an additional role alien to the traditional one of healer. Furthermore, the

psychological context within which health care is delivered would also change, bringing about a fundamental shift in social attitudes to those who suffer long-term illness or disability and who require substantial health resources.

Physician-assisted suicide

In the past, the BMA made no attempt to distinguish between euthanasia and physician-assisted suicide. The two were assumed to be the same, and policy opposing the involvement of doctors in the intentional killing of patients was believed to cover the illegal act of assisting their suicide too.[2] Only in 1997 did the BMA begin to make a distinction when its annual meeting recognised that there is a wide spectrum of views about the issues of physician-assisted suicide and euthanasia and strongly opposed any changes in law for the time being.[3]

In 1998 the BMA's Medical Ethics Department published a discussion paper asking whether the moral arguments about physician-assisted suicide and euthanasia differ, and whether it is morally relevant that in physician-assisted suicide the patient, not the doctor, is the main actor.[4] The same year, the BMA was mandated by its representative body to hold a conference 'to promote the development of a consensus on physician-assisted suicide'. Thus in March 2000, 50 BMA members, representing a range of medical specialties and professional seniority, came together for two days of debate. The consensus statement issued at the end of the conference closely reflects the BMA's policy opposing physician-assisted suicide, whilst recognising that the views of individuals within the profession cover all ends of the spectrum.[5]

This guideline expressing the BMA's views has been updated in the light of the consensus, and extracts from the consensus statement are given in grey boxes throughout the text.

Drawing together a wide range of moral viewpoints and practical considerations, BMA members cannot agree to recommend a change in the law to allow

physician-assisted suicide. Within the profession there is a very wide range of views on physician-assisted suicide (both for and against).

Patient rights

The issue of physician-assisted suicide is often portrayed as a question of 'patient rights', 'free choice' or 'liberty of action'. The BMA considers that this language of choice may belie the real pressures from family members or society in general which may be exerted if assisted suicide were legalised. The BMA believes that patients have a right to make any request they feel appropriate. It cannot be correct for doctors to prevent individuals expressing their desires or asking for their views to be discussed but there is not a con-comitant duty for doctors to meet every request that patients make. This is particularly the case if the patient's request is for the doctor to contravene the rules laid down by the regulatory body, the General Medical Council or the doctor's own conscientiously held views.

Individuals who competently choose to commit suicide are not legally prohibited from doing so, but it does not follow that they have the right to be assisted. Anybody considering suicide has a moral responsibility to take account of the views and feelings of others.

In the context of the debate on physician-assisted suicide, an important moral issue to be considered would be the balance between respect for the patient's autonomous request and any distress and harm that may be caused to those close to the patient.

If the law were to change to permit doctors to end patients' lives on request, participation in assisted suicide would be a matter for the individual doctor's conscience, subject to professional guidance issued by the regulatory body.

The BMA distinguishes between the right that every person has to be supported and cared for during the process of death and the request that patients may make that the doctor should deliberately hasten their death. We believe that there is a clear and indisputable right to care and assistance while dying but we do not believe that patients have a right to insist that doctors end patients' lives.

The BMA emphasises that doctors should accede to a request not to prolong the patient's life by provision of treatment which the patient does not want but the BMA's policy, approved by its membership at several annual representative meetings, is that doctors should not actively intervene to end life or give assistance to this end. If a doctor were to consider the circumstances warranted a deviation from this advice, the BMA considers he or she should be prepared to justify that decision to the General Medical Council or the Courts.

The conference respects the autonomy of competent patients to refuse life-prolonging/sustaining medical treatment and intervention (either contemporaneously or by advance directive). Such competent refusals do not constitute physician-assisted suicide.

The doctor's role

If the law were changed to permit assisted suicide, the BMA would still not wish doctors to be involved because of the effect this would have on the public perception of the medical profession. Although it is quite possible that some doctors would be interested in providing such assistance, the Association would prefer that a separation be maintained between the medical role to sustain life and alleviate suffering by means of palliative care and the function of ending life or assisting suicide. We recognise the emotiveness of the issue but support the view expressed by the distinguished American lawyer Alexander Capron on the subject of euthanasia and echoed by many of the BMA's own members:

'I never want to have to wonder whether the physician coming into my hospital room is wearing the white coat of the healer … or the black hood of the executioner. Trust between patient and physician is simply too important and too fragile to be subjected to the unnecessary strain.'

If physician-assisted suicide were to be practised, it would alter the relationships between doctors and patients, doctors and significant others and doctors and society.

Even though assisted suicide can be distinguished from euthanasia, the BMA would consider an extension of the doctor's role in this direction to challenge the traditional ethos of medicine. The normal duty of the doctor is to attempt to rescue the would-be suicide and considerable moral and practical confusion could be generated by the creation of an option to assist it. The BMA does not believe that physician-assisted suicide is a form of care.

Physicians have a duty to educate about, promote and mobilise maximum support in maintaining quality of life for those for whose life would otherwise be intolerable.

The profession recognises the need for continuing improvement in care of the dying. The conference supports the continued development and provision of high quality palliative care. Physician-assisted suicide should not be considered as an alternative to other forms of care.

Effects on health professionals

While it is difficult, if not impossible, to predict the long-term effect of major social changes, the BMA would be concerned if health professionals were expected to participate in euthanasia or assisted suicide as a result of legal changes. Recent changes in the delivery of health care including the intro-

Role of state and law

The state has an interest in discouraging suicide. The law does not classify attempted suicide as a criminal offence, but the BMA considers that doctors should not assist their patients to commit suicide. The Association would not, therefore support a change in the law on this matter. An anxiety shared by the BMA and other bodies (such as the Canadian Law Commission or the House of Lords Select Committee on Medical Ethics) is the ability of the law to police adequately any such change in a manner which would minimise abuses. Legislation has many advantages, particularly in clarifying society's views. But it can be an error to assume that legislation alone will solve the complex personal and emotional factors which affect the way doctors and patients deal with the most difficult issues.

duction of market forces in the British Health Service have contributed to a distancing between patients and doctors. Competition between health facilities and placing of block contracts by purchasers with the lowest bidder has meant that patients often see different health specialists for every episode of care and lack a sense of continuity. The nature of general practice is also changing with expanded teams of health professionals providing different aspects of care. Ideally, there should be a continuing relationship and trust between individual doctor and patient but the circumstances in which health care is being provided now mean that consultations are often rushed and unsatisfactory to both sides and this ideal of trust and partnership may not be possible in many cases. If the law were to be changed, it is quite conceivable that specialist clinics would cater for this type of procedure and that the discussion would take place as an encounter between strangers with the practitioners having little or no insight into potentially relevant aspects of the individual's past history or rectifiable aspects of the current circumstances.

Part of the BMA's anxiety is also that such a change would give rise to demoralisation among health professionals and ambiguity about their role. If it were part of a health professional's role and duty to assist with suicide and provide advice and counselling for people wishing to carry it out, the underpinning of much of medicine's efforts to improve individual quality of life would be removed.

In addition to the major ethical and moral issues, the conference identified a range of practical problems arising from physician-assisted suicide. These are contained in the consensus statement, which is available on the BMA website or from the Medical Ethics Department (ethics@bma.org.uk).

Requests for further information and all enquiries should be directed to: Medical Ethics Department, British Medical Association, BMA House, Tavistock Square, London WC1H 9JP. Telephone: 020 7383 6286. Fax: 020 7383 6233. E-mail: ETHICS@bma.org.uk

References
1. Report of the Select Committee on Medical Ethics, House of Lords, HMSO 1994.
2. It is unlawful to aid, abet, counsel or procure a suicide under the Suicide Act 1961.
3. BMA Annual Representative Meeting. Edinburgh 1997.
4. British Medical Association. *Euthanasia and physician assisted suicide: Do the moral arguments differ?* London: BMA, April 1998.
5. British Medical Association. *Physician assisted suicide: Statements from a conference to promote the development of a consensus*, 3-4 March 2000. London: BMA, March 2000. Available on the BMA website (www.bma.org.uk).

Euthanasia – the real issues

Dr George Chalmers looks at the issues involved in the current debate

Much of the debate about euthanasia at the present time takes place on a largely philosophical level. As we weigh the arguments, discussing all the pros and cons in the abstract, we can easily miss the real issues.

What are the real issues?

This is about people, not abstractions.

It is very easy to become taken up with the theories, the philosophies, even the ethical arguments, but in the last analysis we are discussing the end of life for individual people. Our responsibility is to meet their real needs, not to justify an opinion or to support a position. Each individual is different, and needs a different answer. We need to get alongside each person and to respond to the challenge of their specific life-situation with life-affirming responses. Death is no answer to any need.

It is about the many, not the few.

The number of cases from which the extreme measure of euthanasia may be argued is very small. If it were to be introduced as an available answer, even to difficult clinical problems, there would be a strong temptation to save resources, time and involvement by bringing life to an end sooner, rather than later. It is the many who will be at risk from such poor decision-making.

It is about the ordinary, not the extraordinary.

The arguments about euthanasia often revolve round the difficult cases, some of them very real and intensely problematic, some of them largely hypothetical. Any lawyer will tell you that 'hard cases make bad law'.

The important issue is that decisions made in the light of extraordinary situations are likely to affect a much broader spectrum of ordinary clinical practice. They could and would be applied to many situations which are currently, and

THE
CHRISTIAN INSTITUTE

CHRISTIAN INFLUENCE IN A SECULAR WORLD

appropriately, handled without recourse to the deliberate ending of life.

It is about compassion, as a standard, not as an exception.

Some time ago a paper appeared in the *British Medical Journal*[1] which reported a study, in which the care of dying patients in four West of Scotland hospitals had been observed. With the full cognisance of medical and nursing staff, a non-participant observer monitored directly the clinical interaction between dying patients and the staff of the wards in which they were treated. The observer was an experienced nursing tutor.

The abstract reads as follows: 'More than half of all patients retained consciousness until shortly before death. Basic interventions to maintain patients' comfort were often not provided: oral hygiene was often poor, thirst remained unquenched and little assistance was given to encourage eating. Contact between nurses and the dying patients was minimal; distancing and isolation of patients by most medical and nursing staff were evident; this isolation increased as death approached.'

Not all of the observed practice was poor. Four of the fourteen consultants and seven of the twenty-two senior nurses were seen to have a greater number of encounters with dying patients than the average. These spent time with the patient, used their name, established eye contact, took steps to meet their clinical and personal needs and maintained contact with them until death.

The others, however, concentrated on the disease process, the physical deterioration and the attempted relief of some of their symptoms. Personal contact was minimal or absent, and it was observed that, as death came nearer, they distanced themselves from the patient. The time spent at a patient's bedside related directly to the continuation of active medical intervention. When this was scaled down and death became imminent, the time given significantly diminished.

The paper cited above reminds us that compassion in the sense of

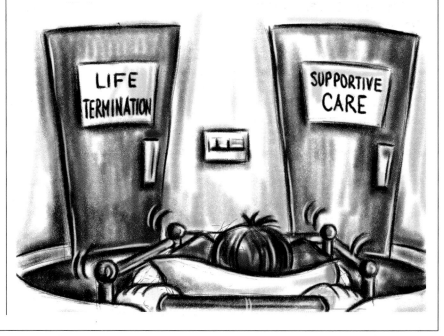

involvement of caring staff is, perhaps, less of a standard than we should like to think. Until there is a level of personal involvement like that demonstrated in the better units, in all caring establishments and situations, dare we risk introducing a 'way out' for the person who does not want to be compassionately involved – even a way out which may be presented as 'compassionate'. We need to ask ourselves:

– Are our standards of care all they might be?
– Are they all we think they are?
– Are they all we claim them to be?

Until they are, whether we like it or not, a case will be made for euthanasia.

It is about how we care for all, not just about the dying.

There is, in fact, little difference between the needs of any seriously ill person and those of the person who is terminally ill. The best answer to complaints of poor care on the one hand, and demands for euthanasia on the other, is the setting of standards of care, which will respond personally and compassionately to the individual, rather than apply a blanket solution to every similar situation. To kill cannot, ever, be a substitute for caring.

Part of the problem lies in quite significant changes in society's attitude to dying. When compared with former attitudes, three such changes are apparent.

Changed attitudes to dying
Non-acceptance
When medical intervention, especially in acutely critical illness, was less likely to be effective, it was more widely accepted that death was likely, and often inevitable. As life-support and resuscitation measures have become more prevalent and effective, this acceptance has been replaced by the expectation that 'Medicine must do something about it', whether the technology or the resources are available or not. The extension of this idea may be 'If Medicine can't do anything about it, let's get it over quickly.'

Secularisation
As religious faith has been eroded by increasingly secular and materialistic philosophies, the view is expressed, 'There is no life, therefore no responsibility after death.' The loss of the idea of personal responsibility for the outcome of life and of a future beyond death, has led to a cheapening of life and a trivialisation of death to the point that it is perceived as merely the end of existence for that individual. The view of the secular agnostic becomes 'If there is nothing after death and no responsibility, there is no reason not to end life.'

Increase in anxiety
One might have expected that such an attitude might reduce anxiety regarding death, but in fact the fear of death persists and has been supplemented by a well-established fear of dying, notably of the process, rather than the fact. This fear relates to the symptoms which the person, may suffer, the fear that suffering may be unrelieved, and the fear also that the process of dying may be unduly prolonged. Many people, when put to it, still fear death and its consequences on the basis of a deep uncertainty about what may lie beyond, an anxiety which can only be relieved by the assurances and the positive hope of faith. Without such faith one might argue, 'If dying is the thing people fear, then it is better to reduce the length of the process.'

Given such reasoning, euthanasia is made to appear as the ultimate in compassionate acts, and the suicide of the terminally ill is given a rationale. The problems that face the introduction of the death option to medical practice are too serious to be set on one side as irrelevant.

Practical problems
The risk of abuse
The reality of possible abuse of power and of clinical freedom is inherent, of course, in all clinical relationships, and the overall risk of deliberate abuse is probably quite small. There is a much greater risk of careless abuse, or of abuse of such a provision by default. If the option to kill the patient were to be available doctors who would not deliberately break the law but interpret it freely will use

it inappropriately. It is easier to 'go along' with the expressed opinion of patients or well-meaning relatives, even if it is expressed under severe emotional duress, than to carefully analyse the clinical options and make a better decision.

Change in relationship
The clinical relationship, by definition, is one of trust. The question must be asked whether it will remain so if the doctor is perceived as one who may bring life to an end.

The doctor's traditional, historic and moral commitment is to LIFE, and the doctor may be most helpful when asserting the value and the meaning of life, when that has been lost to the patient or those around him or her. It is, therefore, a very major change to introduce death as a legitimate clinical option. At present the patient, however distressed, expects the doctor not to suggest death as an option. With legalisation of euthanasia, the fear that he or she might do so introduces further anxiety to the already tense situation of serious illness in a disabled person.

Change in the norm
Legalisation of life termination, under whatever guise, would not only decrease the consideration given to other treatment options, but would also introduce the idea that this is the right, the normal, or indeed the obligatory means of bringing serious illness to an end.

The analogy with the effects of abortion law reform is self-evident. The alternatives available to a teenager or a single woman faced with an unwanted pregnancy are seldom presented when the immediacy of termination is so attractive. The negative consequences are ignored or played down, and the 'easy' way out is accepted as the norm. The girl who opts for any alternative is made to feel abnormal, and indeed may be openly criticised for such a decision. Already there are elderly and disabled people who feel that they are a burden to their relatives or to society as a whole, and who feel an obligation to remove that burden. It is a very sad reflection upon our reputedly compassionate society that such people have such a negative mind-set reinforced by the proposal that the doctor should be free to remove the burden.

How much better would it be to reassert their intrinsic human value by the affirmation of life?

Looking to euthanasia as a primary means to relieve suffering implies losing hope when we most need help to find it. It means concentrating on the loss of one's life instead of on finding meaning in life and turns the focus upon self and suffering at a time when we most need to look beyond them.

There is, then, a real risk that the debate may obscure these issues. We may begin to see withdrawal of treatment, or the assisting of suicide, as the only solution where other valid measures are available. We may see death as the best answer, when asking the wrong questions, or it may seem the easiest solution when the problem of relief becomes demanding.

If we are interested only in winning the debate, having lost sight of the priority of caring for people, the victory will be barren and our society will become less, rather than more, compassionate.

- Mere opposition to euthanasia in the context of debate is not enough! If we are to be active it must also be in the establishment of good, involved, personal care for the ill and disabled, whether terminally ill or not, and of better standards of terminal care in ordinary practice.

Hostel, hospice, community and other supportive care provisions need our support. There is a major need to train and educate doctors, nurses and healthcare workers of every kind, whether in general practice, hospital or nursing homes, towards better supportive care for patients and for relatives.

Reference

1 Mills M et al, Care of Dying Patients in Hospital BMJ, 1994; 309:583-586

Floating clinic will offer the sick offshore euthanasia

By Andrew Osborn in Brussels

A pioneering Australian doctor has unveiled controversial plans to set up the world's first floating euthanasia clinic which would drop anchor off the Australian coast and administer lethal injections or drug dosages to terminally ill patients who wish to die in dignity.

Although the practice is illegal in Australia, Dr Philip Nitschke, a euthanasia campaigner, says he intends to take advantage of the Netherlands' impending decision to legalise euthanasia and buy a Dutch-registered ship so that he can circumvent Australian law.

On Tuesday the Dutch senate is almost certain to back a new law legalising euthanasia, making the Netherlands the first country to allow doctors to assist people in horrific pain with little hope of survival to pass away peacefully.

Nitschke's idea of a floating euthanasia clinic would also be a world first, although a maverick Dutch doctor, Rebecca Gomperts, is in the process of raising finance for the world's first floating abortion clinic, which would drop anchor off the coast of countries such as Ireland where abortion is outlawed. Such projects are expensive and require a panoply of security measures to prevent their opponents trying to sink the ship.

'If this was a Dutch-registered vessel, it would be possible legally to provide access to voluntary euthanasia in international waters,' Nitschke explained yesterday. 'That's the proposal, that we get such a ship and provide assistance to people who would take such an opportunity if such a service existed. I see people all the time and I know that [they] would access it if it was there.'

Once the Dutch senate ratifies the law, Nitschke signalled he would begin raising finance for the controversial project. He rose to prominence when he performed euthanasia on four terminally ill patients after Australia's Northern Territory briefly legalised the practice in 1996.

The federal parliament reversed the law less than a year later, however, and mercy killing remains illegal in Australia. Nitschke continues to hold workshops for terminally ill patients advising them how best they can kill themselves.

The Dutch upper house will begin debating the euthanasia legislation tomorrow but the vote is seen as a formality after the lower house approved the bill in November.

Dutch authorities have turned a blind eye to the practice for decades anyway. Mercy killing is tacitly tolerated in several other countries such as Switzerland and Belgium but none has yet legalised the practice. The US state of Oregon has legalised medically assisted suicide where the doctor gives the patient legal drugs but does not administer them.

The new Dutch law stipulates that eligible patients must be in continuous, unbearable and incurable suffering, be aware of medical alternatives and have demanded a second professional opinion. The request to die must be made voluntarily, independently, persistently and only after careful consideration by a patient judged to be of sound mind.

The law will also allow a patient to make a prior written request for euthanasia, giving doctors the right to use their own discretion when patients become too physically or mentally ill to decide for themselves. Controversially, children aged between 12 and 16 will be able to ask for help to die, but only with parental consent.

The bill is vociferously opposed by the Vatican, religious groups and pro-life campaigners.

Inherent dangers of 'living wills'

Much has been said and written about so-called 'living wills', now more frequently referred to as 'advance directives' or 'advance refusals'. This concept has gained a measure of acceptance both to the public and in medical circles.

Defining our fears

Much of the motivation in setting out our preferences in such a form relates to fears and anxieties over the mode of our dying. It is clearly useful to the doctor, and indeed to other carers as well, to have the priorities, desires and attitudes of the patient made plain. It may even be useful and helpful to write them down. One practitioner of my acquaintance, when asked about a living will, asks the patient to write down the things they are afraid of. The exercise of defining our fears and concerns in this way is often helpful in facing up to them, and in many cases they may be allayed by the doctor, who is quite likely to wish, equally, to spare the patient the very things of which they are afraid.

Restricting the options

Such a document, however, cannot be made binding to cover all possible future events since these cannot be accurately foreseen. Changing circumstances may render it irrelevant, inappropriate or even obstructive to the best care indicated for new circumstances. Where mental capacity has been lost, if such a directive were made binding, the best management may be precluded. To illustrate this I share a recent personal experience.

A dear friend has been suffering progressive weakness and disability from widespread cancer with deposits in bone. At one point in his illness he experienced severe acute pain in one hip, and was found to have a fracture, which had occurred at a point of cancerous infiltration. He

By Dr George Chalmers

was already on high dosage of pain-relieving medication, but this event pushed the pain level through the threshold of relief.

On consultation with an orthopaedic surgeon it was decided, despite his advanced cancer and his debilitated condition, that he should have an operation to 'pin' the fracture and make the hip stable again. He agreed, the operation was done and the extreme pain in his hip was removed.

Had he been incapable of consenting to surgery, and, in particular, if he had previously signed a binding advance refusal of any surgical intervention, he would have been denied the best management of his problem, and would have remained in agony, despite pain relief measures. Euthanasia might then have seemed the only option.

The dangers of binding directives

Like legalised euthanasia, such directives, if held to be binding when applied by others, would be open to abuse and extremely difficult to make safe.

The empowerment of third party proxies to refuse treatment, as suggested in currently proposed legislation, would carry significant risks, especially if the person given such responsibility is not made accountable for the decisions made.

In any system of binding advance directives or refusals, there is no room for change of mind in changing circumstances.

The problem of execution

Like any 'will' type of declaration, a living will would require the agreement and action of the 'Executor', ultimately the doctor with responsibility for the person's care.

Where treatment is refused by someone who can understand, their

autonomy must be respected, but where the consequences are likely to be grave or even fatal, it is essential that they understand fully what they are doing.

For such a decision to be made by a third party, when the person is unable to understand or to consent, the whole area of understanding, motivation, and even of technical knowledge comes into the equation. We cannot say with certainty of anyone else, 'This is what he/she would have wanted'.

While I would never claim infallibility for myself or for any clinical colleague, and while I would never take the position that 'Doctor always knows best', I do believe that a trained and experienced professional person is more likely to make a sound clinical judgment than someone without such knowledge. There is much also to be said for the 'second opinion', or even for the third, fourth or fifth, but these should be informed opinions. A good

relationship in which clear communication takes place between doctor and patient is consistently better than any piece of paper, no matter how well drafted it may be.

Why do people express the wish to die?

The terminally ill person who feels, or states, 'I want to die, I have nothing to live for!' will usually do so for definable reasons. It may be because their illness involves severe pain or other symptoms. They may be depressed, lonely, or feeling a sense of worthlessness. Sometimes it may be a response to the unwanted effects of ineffective 'Curative' therapy.

Most, if not all, of these problems may be addressed by other means than agreeing to kill them.

To change the 'I want to die' attitude will involve giving adequate symptom relief, the drawing of strength from others, providing treatment and support for depression and the introduction of hope to the hopelessness of dying.

In dying we need the love and support of others, who will assert our personal value, and we need balanced palliative care with reduction or cessation of redundant treatment. Where such a regimen is applied relief is obtained and hope restored. The application of the well-established principles of terminal care is an entirely valid alternative to death as a clinical option.

• The above information is an extract from *The Advocate*, the magazine produced by the Christian Institute. See page 41 for their address details.

What's wrong with living wills?

Information from ALERT

Why shouldn't I give instructions here and now about how I want to be treated at the end of my life?
Only your *refusal* of treatment is binding on the doctor.

A Living Will or Advance Directive comes into force when you are unfit to be consulted, and the doctor can decide when that is. If you had been sedated you might be unable to speak for yourself. You might also be unable to feed yourself or pour out a glass of water. If you have signed the most common type of Living Will, a doctor is forbidden to provide intravenous fluids, or tube feeding: it might be considered an assault. This means that you would become dehydrated and die for lack of water.

This could also happen if you were unable to communicate after an accidental injury or a stroke.

The best treatment, aimed at returning you to health, would also be ruled out if you had signed a Living Will. You might live on needlessly disabled.

How can I prevent my life being prolonged artificially?
There is no need to fear this would happen in an NHS hospital, unless your body organs were suitable for transplant. In that case you might be kept on a life-support machine

after you yourself could benefit from it; but only if you had previously signed an organ donor card.

I wouldn't want to live if I couldn't do all the things I used to do.
A lot of people feel that before it happens, but we are more adaptable than we think. If we become disabled we find it's not impossible to cope with it, after all, and life is still worth living.

A study of patients in hospital aged 80 and over, published in the *Journal of the American Medical Association* on 4 February 1998, found that when asked to choose between a shorter lifespan with a higher so-called 'quality of life' or longer lifespan with a lower 'quality', most chose the longer lifespan. '

48% were unwilling to exchange any time in their current state of health for a shorter time in excellent health, and 27.8% were willing to give up at most 1 month of 12 in return for excellent health,' the authors reported.

Do I have a duty to die if I should need nursing care when I get older?

No. It is the duty of other people, in a civilised society, to care for those who need it.

Is death from lack of water an easy way to go?

No, it may take 10 days or more if the patient is not terminally ill. It causes severe kidney pain, among other symptoms. Sedation may not be able entirely to prevent pain and discomfort, though it prevents communication.

In a letter to *The Times* on 28 June 1999 a daughter described what happened to her elderly mother who was taken to hospital with a fractured skull and severe brain damage. At first she was put on an intravenous drip. 'Two and a half weeks later the drip came out of its own accord and was not re-inserted. We were not consulted but did not object because we thought she would die more quickly. We then watched over her for the seven agonising days it took for her to die of dehydration . . . ' The daughter called it an 'appalling end'.

If Living Wills are bad for patients, why do the authorities promote them?

Advance Directives were launched in the USA in 1969 in a law journal article entitled 'Due Process of Euthanasia: The Living Will, a Proposal'. In 1977 Robert Derzon, a Health Dept official, advised President Carter to 'change social values regarding cost-inducing activities', and stated, 'The cost-saving from a nationwide push toward Living Wills is likely to be enormous. Over one-fifth of Medicare expenditures are for persons in their last year of life.' In 1991 it was made compulsory for all patients admitted to hospital in the US, for whatever reason, to be

presented with 'Living Will' forms.

Dr Michael Irwin, a leading member of Britain's Voluntary Euthanasia Society, reported in a letter to the *Journal of the Royal Society of Medicine* (Vol.93, July 2000) that 'When the Dept of Family Medicine at Jefferson Medical College, Philadelphia reviewed the records of 474 Medicare patients who had died in hospital (in 1990, 1991 and 1992) it was discovered that the mean inpatient charge for the 342 patients without documentation of a discussion of advance directives was more than three times that of the 132 patients with such documentation ($95,305 versus $30,478).'

Are Living Wills the only danger to patients?

No. In the USA Steven Becker, aged 29, refused to sign one when he was admitted to hospital for a brain operation in March 2000. After the operation he was considered 'vegetative', although a neurologist thought he might recover. Against some family members' wishes, in September a judge ordered him to be deprived of fluid, and he died. Nancy Valko, a pro-life nurse, commented, 'It makes you wonder why there is such a push to have people sign such documents when not signing one is considered no obstacle to still getting you dead.'

If we become disabled we find it's not impossible to cope with it, after all, and life is still worth living

---

In 1999 the Medical Ethics Committee of the British Medical Association issued guidelines on 'Withholding and Withdrawing Life-prolonging Medical Treatment' in which they informed doctors that it was not only ethical but legal to allow certain categories of patients to die of dehydration, without their having signed a Living Will, and that a court's permission was not needed (this is doubtful). Disabled newborns, patients with Alzheimer's disease and victims of a stroke, who might be fully conscious but unable to swallow properly, were thought to be suitable candidates for death by neglect.

The new Adults with Incapacity (Scotland) Act allows dehydration in the patient's 'best interests' for someone who can't communicate, if a proxy and a doctor agree on this. The English version of the law is expected to be introduced after the next General Election.

How can I avoid mistreatment in hospital which is intended to end my life?

Ann Winterton's Private Member's Bill to prevent such mistreatment was recently 'talked out' in Parliament.

A 'Protective Medical Decisions Document' has been issued in the USA by the International Anti-Euthanasia Task Force (copies are available from ALERT). Although it might not be legally binding on doctors in this country, it would prevent misrepresentation of your wishes if you should be in hospital and unable to speak for yourself.

A Christian 'Advance Declaration for the Management of Serious Illness' in a booklet entitled *Advance Directives or Living Wills*, is available from St Paul's Publications, Morpeth Terrace, London SW1P 1EP.

Write to your Member of Parliament and protest against patients being caused to die by the withholding of water. Britain should do better than this for elderly and defenceless people.

• The above information is from ALERT. See page 41 for their address details.

© *ALERT*

Living wills

Living wills enable you to set out what medical treatment you would not wish to receive if you were unconscious and not going to recover from serious illness or injury

Nowadays, there are many treatments which offer patients with serious or terminal illnesses the chance to live longer. These treatments include kidney dialysis, being fed through a tube or cardio-pulmonary resuscitation (CPR). However, in some cases, these treatments may offer little or no chance of recovery, and they may leave the person in a condition he or she would find unbearable.

Have you ever thought through what you would want to happen if you were seriously ill and unlikely to recover? You may feel strongly that if, for example, you were in a deep coma, or had suffered a massive stroke, you would not wish to receive life-prolonging treatment. However, in this situation you would not be physically or mentally able to talk to your doctors about what you want. This is where a living will comes into use.

What is a living will?

A living will (often known as an 'advance directive' or 'advance refusal') allows you to state which treatments you would or would not want if you became seriously ill in the future and could not say what you wanted to happen.

Living wills usually take the form of a written document, setting out the circumstances under which you would not wish to receive life-prolonging medical treatment. Most standard forms simply need to be completed with your name, address and your GP's contact details. They are then witnessed, and copies lodged with your GP, friends and family. More details about the living will supplied by the VES can be found below.

Some people confuse the issue of refusing treatment under a living will with voluntary euthanasia. The two issues are separate. If you make a living will you are asking doctors not to give you certain medical treatments. Voluntary euthanasia is when you ask the doctor to deliberately end your life.

Valid living wills are legally enforceable

At the moment there is no statute law governing living wills. However, under common law (that is, law decided by the courts), a living will can be legally enforced if it meets the following requirements:

- The person is mentally competent and is over 18 when he or she makes the living will. The person was told all about the nature and effects of refusing treatment at the time he or she made the living will. The living will applies to the circumstances which the patient is in. The person was not encouraged by someone else or wrongly influenced when he or she made the living will. The living will has not been cancelled either verbally or in writing since it was drawn up. The person is now mentally incapable of making decisions because they are unconscious or otherwise incapacitated.

What are the advantages of making a living will?

- A living will makes sure that you will not receive unwanted medical treatment if you are unable to tell doctors your wishes at the time. If you have a living will, your family and friends are not left with difficult decisions when they are not sure what you would have wanted. Knowing what you want will help doctors to make the right decision in difficult circumstances.

Are there any restrictions?

Living wills do have some restrictions. You cannot use them to
1. Refuse basic nursing care which is given to all patients, such as washing; or
2. Ask that staff do not offer you food and drink by mouth.

You cannot refuse treatment if this goes against a valid court order made due to your medical condition.

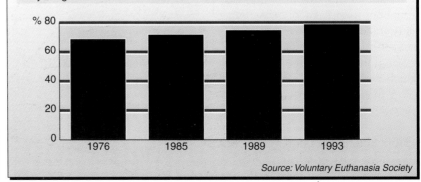

Public opinion survey

Media polls regularly record huge majorities of people who support legalising voluntary euthanasia for the incurably ill. In October 1997, out of nearly 3,000 people who took part in a *Sun* newspaper telephone opinion poll, an amazing 97% said terminally ill people should have the right to die with dignity. The graph below shows the results of large-scale statistical surveys on the topic carried out by NOP (National Opinion Polls).

We asked: 'Some people say that the law should allow adults to receive medical help to an immediate peaceful death if they suffer from an incurable physical illness that is intolerable to them, provided they previously requested such help in writing. Do you agree?'

Source: Voluntary Euthanasia Society

Living wills made by people under 18 do not have the same legal status as those made by adults. However, the Children Act (1989) emphasises that young people's views must be considered in any decisions made about their own treatment. Where possible, the decision should be made jointly between the young person and their parents or legal guardians.

How do I make a living will?

If you would like to make a living will, there are several standard forms available. The Voluntary Euthanasia

Society form is available to download for free, along with full instructions on how to complete it. Alternatively, a living will pack (three living will forms, answers to frequently asked questions, a carrying card to notify others of your living will, and full

instructions on completing the forms) can be obtained for £5 from the VES office. Please note, however, that these forms are only suitable for use in the UK. Simply send a cheque or postal order for £5, making sure you include your name and full address, to: VES, 13 Prince of Wales Terrace, London, W8 5PG

Resuscitation attempts and your living will

Resuscitation is successful in only a minority of patients – and it is a procedure that many do not wish to endure. Here, we look at the guidelines covering resuscitation attempts both in and out of hospital

Resuscitation, CPR, DNR: all these terms have been in common usage by the media in recent months. With all this press attention, the debate about resuscitation and when it should or should not be carried out has become mixed up with allegations of ageism within the NHS. In this article, we look at what resuscitation actually is, the guidelines covering its application in both hospital and out-of-hospital settings, and how your living will affects do-not-resuscitate decisions.

What is resuscitation?

Cardiopulmonary resuscitation ('CPR' for short) is an overarching term for a number of techniques used to try and restart a heart which has stopped beating. In theory, therefore, CPR could be used on every one of us, eventually. However, in reality, medical teams must decide which patients might respond to CPR before they dash in to try and restart a heart.

How successful is it?

Recent newspaper reports have talked about the 'denial' of CPR to

By Jenni Burt

elderly patients as though it is something that guarantees a return to life. This reveals a deep misunderstanding of what CPR actually is, and what it can do. In an extensive study of resuscitation in British hospitals, researchers found only 17% of patients who receive CPR on general wards actually

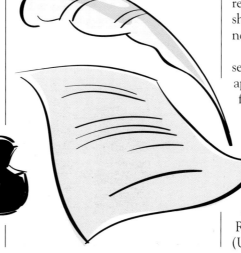

survive to be discharged, and 13% are still alive one year on.[1] This figure drops to 5% one-year survival if the cardiac arrest happens outside of hospital. As this shows, resuscitation attempts are successful only in a certain group of patients; for many, illness, old age and general infirmity will impact on the likelihood of a 'return to life' after their heart has stopped beating. The procedure can have complications such as broken ribs and the risk of brain damage. At a recent meeting of nurses I attended, every one had witnessed one or more resuscitation attempts that simply should not have been started. CPR is not a miracle worker.

Recognising that limits must be set about when an attempt at CPR is appropriate, the new 'NHS plan' put forward by the Government in July of this year stressed that all NHS organisations must implement local resuscitation policies from next year (although many do already have these in place). These will be based on guidelines issued by the BMA, RCN and Resuscitation Council (UK) in June 1999.

Why might a non-resuscitation policy be recorded for a patient?

The joint guidance on resuscitation published by the BMA and RCN sets out the following four scenarios when CPR will not be appropriate:

1. When CPR will not be successful due to the patient's condition.
2. When a competent patient has refused CPR.
3. When an incompetent patient has refused CPR through a living will.
4. When, if CPR were successful, it will be followed by a length and quality of life which will not be in the best interests of the patient.

Therefore, if you have a living will and are being treated in hospital, a resuscitation attempt should not be made if your heart stops beating as long as your living will applies to the circumstances you are in. The VES continues to campaign for wider understanding of living wills amongst medical staff, to ensure that all such documents are respected. It is good news that the government is insisting all NHS organisations follow the BMA recommendations, which stress that valid living wills refusing resuscitation must be respected.

What about emergency medicine?

However, hospital guidelines on when not to attempt resuscitation do not extend to the paramedics and ambulance crew who might be called in an emergency. The first priority for ambulance personnel is to take action. A living will does not and cannot prevent paramedics from starting CPR on a patient.

The VES living will is not designed for emergency out-of-hospital situations. It asks for treatment to be withdrawn or withheld only if '…two independent doctors (one a consultant) are of the opinion that I am unlikely to recover from illness or impairment involving severe distress or incapacity for rational existence'. This is not a condition that can be met in an emergency situation.

Can the living will be altered?

Even if the 'doctors only' requirement were to be removed from your living

will, this would not enable ambulance personnel to cease or withhold treatment. If an ambulance is called, the crew are obliged to start resuscitation on a patient unless there are visible signs of death (i.e. decomposition or rigor mortis).

Living wills are a powerful tool for ensuring a patient's wishes are respected, within the right setting

---

For example, the London Ambulance Service follows strict protocols on how they react to any emergency situation. Their job is to save life. Under protocol ETO 11, Recognition of Adult Death, ambulance crew will immediately start resuscitation on a patient whose heart has stopped. The only possible situation where they might not start CPR is if a patient's GP or a hospital clinician can, without delay, confirm that it is against the patient's wishes to be resuscitated. Crews can only act on the advice of a doctor in this regard. There is no provision in their guidelines for do-not-resuscitate orders to be acted upon without confirmation from a GP.

So what can I do?

The simple answer is – make sure an ambulance is not called. If an

ambulance crew arrive on the scene where a patient's heart has stopped, they will commence CPR. They have to: if precious seconds are lost whilst searching for a patient's views on resuscitation, people who would wish to be treated could die unnecessarily.

Living wills are a powerful tool for ensuring a patient's wishes are respected, within the right setting. The guidelines on resuscitation in hospitals necessarily differ greatly from those governing emergency, out-of-hospital medicine. DNR orders made within hospitals should be made after careful consideration, by a senior clinician and following set guidelines; and in this situation, your living will should be respected. But if your heart stops beating outside of hospital, and an ambulance is called, they will do all they can to save your life; in an emergency, act first, ask questions later.

References:
1. Tunstall-Pedoe et al 1992 'Survey of 3765 cardiopulmonary resuscitations in British Hospitals. The BRESUS Study: methods and overall results'. *British Medical Journal.* 304, 1347-1351.

• The above information is an extract from the Voluntary Euthanasia Society's web site which can be found at www.ves.org.uk Alternatively see page 41 for their address details.

© *Voluntary Euthanasia Society (VES)*

Report casts new doubt on living wills

*By Sarah Boseley,
Health Correspondent*

A young woman who had told her family that she would rather die than live in a persistent vegetative state, changed her opinion completely after a car accident left her with such severe brain damage that doctors wrongly thought she was unaware of the world around her and applied to the courts to withdraw feeding.

The life of Ms X – her identity has not been disclosed – was reportedly saved by Tom McMillan, a clinical neuropsychologist at Glasgow university, who devised tests to establish whether she had any level of understanding.

He found a way of communicating with Ms X and discovered that in spite of her very low quality of life, she wanted to live.

Prof McMillan says his work with the patient, revealed in the week that the Scottish parliament is debating new legislation on euthanasia and the mentally incapacitated, shows the danger of 'living wills'.

Ms X was 22 when she was badly injured in a car accident. For months it was thought she was in a persistent vegetative state – the same condition as that suffered by Tony Bland after the Hillsborough football stadium disaster.

Mr Bland's family and the hospital where he was being treated successfully applied to the courts to stop tube-feeding him and he died.

'If you do a poll and ask people how they would feel, usually they say they would prefer to die. When they make a living will, that is what people usually say.

'But once somebody is disabled, their point of view can be completely different. Their interests and motivations have become very different,' he said.

The case is likely to stoke the controversy caused by guidelines released by the British Medical Association last year, which suggested that doctors, together with families, could make decisions about when to stop the treatment of a patient. After four or five months, it was thought that Ms X could move a limb or open or shut an eye in response to a request. But doctors felt her cognitive functioning was only just above PVS level.

> **'But once somebody is disabled, their point of view can be completely different. Their interests and motivations have become very different'**

'The weight of medical opinion in this case was that feeding should be terminated,' said Prof McMillan.

Her family said that she had, in effect, given a 'living will' when they had discussed the Bland case. They assumed she would not want to go on living.

Prof McMillan was called in to find out how much awareness Ms X had. He found that she could press a buzzer with her knuckles and he devised a series of questions, with yes or no answers, that established her level of understanding and her will to live.

Prof McMillan feels that an independent neuropsychological assessment of any patient in a similar condition and where the will to live is in doubt should be mandatory.

In the light of this case, he says, 'it is difficult to maintain an argument that it is for the doctor to decide where the line should be drawn'.

His first assessment of Ms X was published in the journal *Brain Injury* in 1996. Prof McMillan has now re-assessed his patient and found significant improvements in her abilities, even though her quality of life to most people would appear very poor.

She can now speak, although neither well nor loudly, she has limited vision and limited movement in her right arm. She is totally dependent on 24-hour nursing care.

But, writes Prof McMillan in a recent edition of *Brain Injury*, 'despite greater insight into her condition, low mood and pain, it is of note that she continues to state that she wishes to continue living.

'Her consistent wish to live post-injury supports the view that beliefs which are common pre-injury and may be expressed [in a living will] can change radically after brain damage.'

A bill now before the Scottish parliament is designed to clarify legal and medical issues around the treatment of people who do not have the mental capacity to make decisions for themselves. An amendment which would forbid the stopping of food or fluid with the express intent to cause death has been proposed.

We'd like living wills, say most pensioners

By Jenny Hope

Most elderly people would like to make a 'living will' setting out whether they should be allowed to die if they become too ill to communicate, say researchers.

They also found that the vast majority of pensioners do not want their lives prolonged if they develop a terminal illness.

In the first study of its kind in Britain, the researchers interviewed 74 elderly patients aged between 66 and 97 at two hospitals to find out their views on living wills.

Almost all the patients had to have the idea explained to them. But when it was, many were interested in leaving written instructions about the type of medical care they wanted if they were unable to speak for themselves. Ninety-two per cent said they wanted to register in advance that they would no longer wish their lives to be prolonged by doctors. At the end of a terminal disease, more than nine out of ten patients would refuse surgery, artificial feeding, ventilation and resuscitation.

Almost as many were against having intravenous fluids or antibiotics, according to the researchers, who specialise in care of the elderly at Imperial College School of Medicine in Central London.

Many disabilities were unacceptable to the patients, such as being bed bound, doubly incontinent or unable to speak, says the study, reported in the *British Medical Journal* today.

Many patients said they would prefer 'comfort-only' care to active treatment – even if it meant they might die. The most feared condition was advanced dementia, while the least was being in a wheelchair.

> ## 'Many welcomed the opportunity to talk about end-of-life issues, especially to someone outside the family'

Around three-quarters expressed interest in writing living wills, which are also known as advance directives. One of the main reasons was to relieve the burden on their family of taking decisions. Dr Rebekah Schiff, one of the research team, said: 'We rarely see living wills on wards for the elderly, even though they are the age group that might benefit from having their views about medical intervention recorded in advance.

'We wondered whether they were not interested, or just didn't know much about them – and it turns out they do want to know more.

'Many welcomed the opportunity to talk about end-of-life issues, especially to someone outside the family. Often there is too little time on a busy ward for these things to be discussed, yet they are surrounded by people who are being faced with these kinds of decisions.

'Some muddled up a living will with euthanasia and some wrongly believed euthanasia was routinely practised in Britain, when it cannot legally be done.

'When we made it clear we were talking about the difference between active care and letting Nature take its course, the majority wanted comfort-only care.'

Jenni Burt, of the Voluntary Euthanasia Society, said it receives about 1,000 requests a week for copies of a standard living will form.

The biggest problem is that no Act of Parliament governs their use, only common law. This has less force, although legal precedents show doctors are bound by a living will that meets certain conditions – such as lack of pressure in making it.

*© The Daily Mail
June, 2001*

ADDITIONAL RESOURCES

You might like to contact the following organisations for further information. Due to the increasing cost of postage, many organisations cannot respond to enquiries unless they receive a stamped, addressed envelope.

Age Concern England
Astral House
1268 London Road
London, SW16 4ER
Tel: 020 8679 8000
Fax: 020 8765 7211
E-mail: ace@ace.org.uk
Web site: www.ageconcern.org.uk
Age Concern information line
provides a service to older people.
Freephone 0800 009966 open 7
days a week, 7am to 7pm.

ALERT
27 Walpole Street
London, SW3 4QS
Tel: 020 7730 2800
Fax: 020 7730 1710
E-mail: alert@donoharm.org.uk
Web site: www.donoharm.org.uk/alert
The aim of ALERT is to warn
people of the dangers of any type of
euthanasia legislation and pro-
death initiatives.

**British Humanist Association
(BHA)**
47 Theobald's Road
London, WC1X 8SP
Tel: 020 7430 0908
Fax: 020 7430 1271
E-mail: info@humanism.org.uk
Web site: www.humanism.org.uk
The British Humanist Association
is the UK's leading organisation for
people concerned with ethics and
society, free from religious and
supernatural dogma.

Canadian Physicians for Life
10150 Gillanders Road
Chilliwack
BC V2P 6H4, Canada
Tel: 00 604 794 3772
Fax: 00 604 794 3960
E-mail: info@physiciansforlife.ca
Web site: www.physiciansforlife.ca
Founded in 1975, Canadian
Physicians for Life are a non-profit,
charitable organisation of
Canadian physicians dedicated to
the respect and ethical treatment
of every human being, regardless of
age or infirmity.

Catholic Media Office (CMO)
39 Eccleston Square
London, SW1V 1BX
Tel: 020 7828 8709
Fax: 020 7931 7678
E-mail: cmo@cbcew.org.uk
Web site: www.catholic-ew.org.uk
The Catholic Media Office is the
press and publications office of the
Catholic Bishops' Conference of
England and Wales.

**Christian Medical Fellowship
(CMF)**
Partnership House
157 Waterloo Road
London, SE1 8XN
Tel: 020 7928 4694
Fax: 020 7620 2453
E-mail: info@cmf.org.uk
Web site: www.cmf.org.uk
A network of approximately 4,500
doctors and 600 medical students
throughout the UK and Republic
of Ireland which opposes
euthanasia.

First Do No Harm
Doctors Who Respect Human Life
PO Box 17317
London, SW3 4WJ
Tel: 01481 264103
Fax: 01481 264162
E-mail: enquiries@donoharm.org.uk
Web site: www.donoharm.org.uk
The aim of 'First Do No Harm' is
to bring together doctors who are
opposed to the current campaign
for euthanasia, and to exchange
information.

Partnership for Caring
National Office
1620 Eye Street NW, Suite 202
Washington, DC 20007, USA
Tel: 00 1 202 296 8071
Fax: 00 1 202 296 8352
E-mail: pfc@partnershipforcaring.org
Web site:
www.partnershipforcaring.org
US-based national non-profit
organisation that partners
individuals and organisations in a
powerful collaboration to improve
how people die in society.

ProLife Alliance
PO Box 13395
London, SW3 6XE
Tel: 020 7351 9955
Fax: 020 7349 0450
E-mail: info@prolife.org.uk
Web site: www.prolife.org.uk
The ProLife Alliance seeks to ensure
the right to life of all, the most basic
and fundamental human right.

**Society for the Protection of
Unborn Children (SPUC)**
Phyllis Bowman House
5-6 St Matthew Street
London, SW1P 2 JT
Tel: 020 7222 5845
Fax: 020 7222 0630
E-mail: enquiry@spuc.org.uk
Web site: www.spuc.org.uk
SPUC campaigns against threats to
the right to live: especially abortion
and euthanasia.

**South Australian Voluntary
Euthanasia Society (SAVES)**
PO Box 2151, Kent Town
SA 5071, Australia
Fax: 00 61 8 8265 2287
E-mail: info@saves.asn.au
Web site: www.saves.asn.au
SAVES' primary objective is a change
to the law in South Australia.

The Christian Institute
26 Jesmond Road
Newcastle Upon Tyne, NE2 4PQ
Tel: 0191 281 5664
Fax: 0191 281 4272
E-mail: info@christian.org.uk
Web site: www.christian.org.uk
A non-denominational Christian
organisation, concerned with the
family, education and pro-life
issues and religious liberties.

Voluntary Euthanasia Society
13 Prince of Wales Terrace
London, W8 5PG
Tel: 020 7937 7770
Fax: 020 7376 2648
E-mail: info@ves.org.uk
Web site: www.ves.org.uk
The Voluntary Euthanasia Society
(UK) campaigns for wider choice
at the end of life.

INDEX

★ ★ ★ ★ ★

The Internet has been likened to shopping in a supermarket without aisles. The press of a button on a web browser can bring up thousands of sites but working your way through them to find what you want can involve long and frustrating on-line searches.

And unfortunately many sites contain inaccurate, misleading or heavily biased information. Our researchers have therefore undertaken an extensive analysis to bring you a selection of quality web site addresses.

Voluntary Euthanasia Society
www.ves.org.uk
VES has a wide range of factsheets on its web site including the following Campaigns, The Law, Press and Factsheets. Factsheets are availble to download as PDFs. There is also a section dedicated to Living Wills.

CARE (Christian Action Research and Education)
www.care.org.uk
CARE has produced a range of briefing papers to enable Christians to understand quickly a wide range of issues. A number of these are available on-line including *Euthanasia – and End of Life Issues*. You can view the briefing papers by clicking on Resources from the home page.

The Ultimate Pro-Life Resource List
www.prolifeinfo.org
Ultimate, founded in April 1995, has become one of the most comprehensive listing of right to life information on the Internet. Clicking on Euthanasia on the home page takes you to a listing of information they have on euthanasia and assisted-suicide from the US and around the world.

Exit
www.euthanasia.org
This site contains hundreds of pages of material explaining the arguments for and against euthanasia. It is promoted by Exit (formerly the Scottish Voluntary Euthanasia Society), which campaigns for a change in British law to promote individual patient choice, and strategies for improved palliative care and other resources at the end of life.

Euthanasia.Com
www.euthanasia.com
A US based site which is committed to the fundamental belief that the direct killing of another person is wrong. The site has information on euthanasia, physician-assisted suicide, living wills, and mercy killing. A huge site.

Christian Medical Fellowship (CMF)
www.cmf.org.uk
CMF produces literature addressing a wide range of ethical issues from a Christian perspective. The Site Index provides links to articles on numerous ethicals topics including euthanasia.

ACKNOWLEDGEMENTS

The publisher is grateful for permission to reproduce the following material.

While every care has been taken to trace and acknowledge copyright, the publisher tenders its apology for any accidental infringement or where copyright has proved untraceable. The publisher would be pleased to come to a suitable arrangement in any such case with the rightful owner.

Chapter One: The Moral Views

A non-religious perspective on voluntary euthanasia, © British Humanist Association (BHA), Euthanasia definitions, © Voluntary Euthanasia Society, The case against euthanasia, © Voluntary Euthanasia Society, The case for euthanasia, © Voluntary Euthanasia Society, Euthanasia and the Catholic Church, © Catholic Media Office (CMO), Worries about allowing assisted death, © Age Concern England on behalf of the Millennium Debate of the Age, Euthanasia, © Society for the Protection of the Unborn Child (SPUC), Brief answers to five objections, © South Australian Euthanasia Society (SAVES), Physician-assisted suicide, © Christian Medical Fellowship (CMF), Dutch pass euthanasia bill, © Guardian Newspapers Limited 2001, Man tells radio show how he killed mother, © Guardian Newspapers Limited 2000, Why I killed my mother, © Guardian Newspapers Limited 2000, Allow these women to die with dignity, beg families, © The Daily Mail, October 2000, 'We can have a choice about dying', © 2000 The Independent Newspaper (UK) Ltd, Public opinion on euthanasia, © Voluntary Euthanasia Society, Glossary of terms, © 2001 Partnership for Caring, Inc., Euthanasia kills . . . , © ProLife Alliance, Dutch MPs back euthanasia law, © Telegraph Group Limited, London 2000.

Chapter Two: The Medical Dilemma

Medical debate, © 2001 The Independent Newspaper (UK) Ltd, Survey of medical opinion, © Voluntary Euthanasia Society, First do no harm, © First Do No Harm, Trust me, I'm a doctor . . . , © Telegraph Group Limited, London 2000, 'Do no harm' abandoned in Holland, © Canadian Physicians for Life, End of life decisions, © British Medical Association (BMA), Euthanasia – the real issues, © The Christian Institute, Floating clinic will offer the sick offshore euthanasia, © The Observer/Guardian Newspapers Limited 2001.

Chapter Three: Living Wills

Inherent dangers of 'living wills', © The Christian Institute, What's wrong with living wills?, © ALERT, Living wills, © Voluntary Euthanasia Society, Public opinion survey, © Voluntary Euthanasia Society, Resuscitation attempts and your living will, © Voluntary Euthanasia Society, Report casts new doubt on living wills, © Guardian Newspapers Limited 2000, We'd like living wills, say most pensioners, © The Daily Mail, June 2001.

Photographs and illustrations:

Pages 1, 5, 11, 15, 30, 38: Pumpkin House, pages 4, 7, 13, 24, 27, 33, 40: Simon Kneebone.

Craig Donnellan
Cambridge
September, 2001